BLOOD, SWEAT & TEARS

GLENYS SPRAY is a journalist who specialises in women's issues. She is a trained social anthropologist with a keen awareness of the influences and attitudes that affect and shape women's lives. Actively involved with women's groups, she was a founder member of the Women's Collective in Cork in the late 1970s, and is a delegate to the National Women's Council and a member of the Cork Women's Poetry Circle. A mother of two school-going children, she has followed the hepatitis C scandal closely. In recording the heart-rending stories of the women and men affected by this major public health scandal, she illustrates the courage and resilience of all ordinary people who refuse to be side-tracked in their fight for justice.

Blood, Sweat & Tears

The Hepatitis C Scandal

Glenys Spray

WOLFHOUND PRESS
& in the US and Canada
The Irish American Book Company

First published in 1998 by
Wolfhound Press Ltd
68 Mountjoy Square
Dublin 1, Ireland
Tel: (353-1) 874 0354
Fax: (353-1) 872 0207

Published in the US and Canada by
The Irish American Book Company
6309 Monarch Park Place
Niwot, Colorado 80503, USA
Tel: (303) 652-2710
Fax: (303) 652-2689

British Library Cataloguing in Publication Data
A catalogue record for this book is available from the British Library.

ISBN 0-86327-647-4

The names of some of those interviewed have been changed to protect their
identity.

10 9 8 7 6 5 4 3 2 1

Cover Photograph: Slide File
Cover Design: Slick Fish Design
Typesetting: Wolfhound Press
Printed in the Republic of Ireland by Colour Books, Dublin

Contents

To my children, Aisling and Oisín

Prologue

On the Japanese island of Miyajimi there is a Buddhist shrine with a sacred red box. The box has four holes, labelled according to different blood groups. For a few yen, visitors to the island can reach inside the appropriate section and pull out a message containing their fortune. They can discover who to marry, who to avoid. It is believed that different blood groups give rise to different personalities. Some will be compatible, others would make for a disastrous match.

History is filled with strange and mysterious customs, rites and taboos concerning blood. Cave paintings show arrows pointing at the heart of hunters; Romans fought fiercely for a drop of blood from the victorious gladiator; in Mexico and Peru the punishment for sexual offences included a symbolic act of drawing blood from those found to be guilty; and in Aztec culture, there was the ultimate symbolic act — human sacrifice, where blood was required for the appeasement of the sun god. Amongst the Bedouin, the daughter of the nearest relative of a murderer is required as 'blood price', becoming the property of the son, brother or father of the slain.

Traditionally, blood has been seen as a perilous and menacing substance, requiring strong ritual cleansing. It is, therefore, no coincidence that Judaic, Islamic and Christian religions all contain prohibitions, many involving women and menstrual blood. In Leviticus it is said that touching a menstruating woman, or anything she sits on, requires washing and the presentation of a sin offering.

And until very recently, in our own culture, women who had given birth were allowed to enter Catholic churches only after they had been symbolically cleansed, or 'churched'.

Blood is potent, powerful and symbolic — the very stuff of life, and of death. It is at once associated with good and evil, saints and sinners. The stigmata, a condition, bestowed upon the saintly, is said to be revealed by blood oozing from those same places where the dying Christ was wounded during his crucifixion. It comes only with suffering and pain. Today, the blood of Christ is still symbolically celebrated.

In literature there are also strong mysterious images associated with blood. Shakespeare's Lady Macbeth wrings her hands, feverishly trying to wash away the tainted blood of her husband's victim. In *The Merchant of Venice*, Shylock implores: 'If you prick us do we not bleed?' Faust's pact with the devil is written in blood. In *Anatomie of the World*, poet John Donne writes: 'Mollifie it with they teares, or sweat or blood'.

The potency of blood as a powerful symbol has not been lost on politicians either. In 1866, British Prime Minister Gladstone described African history as being, for the most part, 'written in blood and tears'. Later, in 1940, Winston Churchill told a nation, 'I have nothing to offer but blood, toil, tears and sweat.' And in the 1960s, British Conservative MP Enoch Powell stirred the racial cauldron with his speech warning of 'rivers of blood'.

Even the day-to-day language we use reflects the deeper human significance of blood. We talk of blood feuds, bad blood, blood brothers, young blood, and of personalities as cold or hot-blooded. Blood, it is said, is thicker than water.

More than being a simple body fluid, blood is at the very essence of our humanity. Powerful and unseen, it can kill or cure. In the womb the unborn baby is nourished through the flow of its mother's blood, and now, through DNA testing, we can begin to play god, to discover the sex of the newly created foetus. It is no wonder then, that blood evokes such strong, soul-deep emotions and makes us ask questions that are at the very centre of our being.

So, when 1,600 women and men discovered that they had been infected with hepatitis C through a contaminated blood product, the impact on them was shattering. There was the shocking realisation that they were now living with a life-threatening disease — an insidious and unpredictable disease. And there was the tortuous uncertainty about what the future might hold. Many felt a deep sense of violation. Some described the feeling of a sinister and dark force inside their bodies. The psychological impact was enormous. Together with their own anxiety and sense of isolation, they also had to face the deep-rooted fear and prejudice of others — a fear that has always served to stigmatise and exclude those with 'tainted blood'.

Chapter One

A Rude Awakening
22 February 1994

It's 8.30 a.m. David Hanly and the *Morning Ireland* team are about to tackle the main item of the day — an urgent call from the Blood Transfusion Service Board for women who were administered the Anti-D blood product in 1977 to attend the Blood Bank for testing.

Mary, who works as a confectioner, brushes the flour from her fingers, and turns up the volume on her transistor. She has already been sent a letter by the Blood Bank, asking her to come in, but she didn't pay too much heed. As a regular blood donor, she has received requests like this before. They might be in touch if there's a shortage. This time she wonders what it is all about.

When she hears the words 'scare', and 'shock' being used, her ears prick up. 'Is that me they're talking about?' she asks herself. 'Am I a part of all this?'

Mechanically, she keeps on working, kneading the dough for a batch of bread to be sold in the shop below. 'Contamination', 'virus', 'thousands of women facing tests' — the words spin round in Mary's head. Each minute brings with it an increasing sense of misgiving.

In the shop she spots her family GP, a no-nonsense man who has been treating her for years. Surely he'll know what's going on.

'Did you hear the radio?' she asks over the counter.

'Do you think that might be me they're talking about?'

He shakes his head.

'I can't help. I'm completely in the dark,' he says. 'As soon as you've been to the Blood Bank, come back to me. I need to know what's happening. I've been inundated with phone calls this morning.'

Panic sets in.

Twelve noon. Mary can't stand the anxiety any longer. She phones her husband, leaves work early, and together they head for the Blood Bank.

Outside, the weather is freezing. A real February day, with patches of light snow and blustery cold winds. At the Blood Bank, Mary sees a steady flow of women coming and going. Inside there is chaos — phones ringing non-stop, nurses rushing from one room to another, receptionists giving out the freephone helpline number to callers. Queues of women sit waiting, some chatting to their neighbours, others sitting alone and anxious. No one seems to know what's happening. Forms are being given out. There are questions about children's names, hospitals attended, and more intimate details about ear piercing, tattoos, even the history of sexual partners. Mary can feel the tension air-borne.

> *I could sense that those women were all apprehensive, even if they weren't saying so. Some, like me, were clearly worried sick.*

Spotting a woman she knows, Mary nods, and then turns away, not wanting to talk.

> *All the time I kept trying to find out what was happening, what this was about, but no one wanted to explain.*

A nurse approaches: 'You're not having the first test. We already have a sample.'

Mary cringes. Why is such personal information being

given in front of all these people? She begins to feel like an outcast.

'Are you the lady who has tested positive?' a young doctor asks loudly.

'Everyone seems to know what's happened except me,' Mary thinks, fear and confusion mixing with anger.

> *By this time I was really freaking. I felt as if everyone was ganging up on me.*

To top it all, a voice behind her pipes up: 'The very person I'm looking for. You're one of the hepatitis women aren't you? Can I take a photograph for my paper?'

An hour later, after she has done a great deal of badgering in reception, she finally meets Dr Joan Power, Consultant Haematologist with the Blood Transfusion Service Board.

'We tested your blood for hepatitis C and it's coming out positive,' Dr Power says. 'Your last test was "scruffy". It's not looking good.'

Mary stares at her husband in disbelief. 'What does it mean?' she manages to whisper.

The nightmare scenario she's being given is unreal — liver biopsy, cirrhosis, liver transplant. The words begin to spin around in her head. She is told to keep spotlessly clean, to keep toothbrushes separate, to be extra careful with tampons and sanitary towels, to use bleach to mop up blood spills.

> *I was looking at my husband saying, 'This can't be true. Tell me I'm dreaming.'*

To make things worse, Dr Power keeps using the letters HCV. This really scares Mary. 'It's only one letter away from HIV,' she thinks.

Sitting in the car outside, Mary is in a state of shock. The picture is getting blacker by the minute. Most frightening is the suspicion that she isn't being told the truth.

> *It was all evasive, ifs, buts and maybes. I felt like some sort of anonymous guinea pig, part of an experiment with test tubes and bottles. Not once that morning did anyone ask me how I was doing, how I felt.*

Questions come in floods: what about my four children — could they be infected? Is my husband all right? Where has all the blood that I donated gone to? Did I give bad blood to someone else? How long have they known I was infected? Is this thing suddenly going to attack me? If it's been eating away at me all this time. what damage has it done?

Then comes bleak desolation. Mary asks herself whether she will even be around in six months' time.

> *I had this picture of the inside of my body: black and gloomy. I could feel this thing moving around, eating away at me. A menacing voice inside me said, 'If you're being told to keep your toothbrush separate, it must be very bad.'*

Niggling away is something else she heard said several times this morning: 'The good thing is that the women we'll catch in this screening are all well women.'

But Mary's experience contradicts this. 'I'm not well,' she thinks. 'I haven't been well for years.' The penny is slowly beginning to drop. Is the BTSB protecting itself, attempting to evade responsibility? Memories come surging back: all those inexplicable aches and pains, those stomach and bowel problems, the tingling in her arms, and that awful, bone-deep tiredness that's been there for so long. 'Women's problems,' she was told. 'If you have children, you must expect to feel tired. Go home and rest.'

Chapter Two

The Woman
Behind the Screen

In a sterile government office in Adelaide Road, Judge Finlay hears evidence from seventy-one witnesses. They include high-ranking officials from the Blood Transfusion Service Board, the Department of Health, the National Drugs Advisory Board, and two government ministers. Most chilling is the testimony of survivors, ordinary women and men, who tell their own harrowing stories — stories without happy endings. This is no ordinary tribunal; it is about life and death. To a shocked, silent room of people, witnesses describe how their lives have changed irrevocably — lives that will continue to be filled with pain and suffering long after the lawyers have packed up their files, and Judge Finlay's report has been consigned to the dusty shelves of libraries.

> Q. Now, I cannot see you, can you hear me?

> A. Yes, I can.

> Q. You are obviously a female person?

> A. Correct.

> Q. What age are you?

> A. Forty.

> Q. Have you been diagnosed as being hepatitis C positive?

A. I have, yes.

Q. When was that diagnosis made?

A. 1989.

A shadowy voice speaks out from behind a screen. It fills the deathly quiet of the room where rows of grey-suited lawyers scribble notes, pass messages, search through bulky files. Sitting alone, Judge Thomas Finlay, head bowed, listens intently to the testimony of this witness, a middle-aged mother. She is nervous about telling her story, in case emotion overcomes her. And she's scared in case someone discovers her identity. It has taken a lot of courage for her to come forward.

Packed into the back of the room are other survivors of what has come to be regarded by many as the biggest scandal in the history of the state. They strain to catch the faltering disembodied voice of the witness as she struggles to give her testimony. They share her pain. Her story is one with an all-too-familiar ring to it.

Since she was an infant, the woman explains, she has been dogged by kidney problems. One of her first memories is of being on a dialysis machine, attached to an artificial kidney. She has had four kidney transplants. The first, in 1977, was of an organ donated by her mother. It lasted for nine years.

When she was on dialysis the woman received numerous transfusions to counteract anaemia and to put iron back into her blood. Her third transplant, in 1994, was not a success — the kidney clotted and, as a result, she experienced a massive coronary.

'It was horrific,' she recalls. 'I was pronounced practically dead, but thankfully because of a very good team of doctors and nurses I pulled through.' Two days later another kidney was transplanted. She still has it.

Despite such enormous physical and mental turmoil,

this woman was coping. She was also learning to come to terms with marriage breakdown, and with the daunting, demanding, task of bringing up her seventeen-year-old son on her own. Then she received a letter from the Blood Bank telling her that she had hepatitis C.

The voice is stronger now. Anger is making it stronger. But it's impossible not to detect an underlying sadness, a certain feeling of hopelessness. After all she has been through, all she has survived, she has now been dealt this second, cruel blow.

> Q. You would be in a happy position, as happy as you could be having regard to your difficulties, but for your unfortunate hepatitis C?
>
> A. That is correct.
>
> Q. Now, perhaps you would be kind enough to inform the Tribunal as to how, from your perspective as a person who is dealing with the difficulties that you have had dealt to you by virtue of the kidney problems, that you carry an extra load. . . .
>
> A. As a result of the hepatitis C my whole lifestyle has changed. Once you have a renal transplant you are effectively normal again, the same as anybody else walking the streets. But with hepatitis C that has not happened. The kidney is functioning perfectly and my blood tests in respect of the kidney are perfect, but I have a lot of other symptoms that are non-related and it makes life very, very difficult.

There is a pause. The woman describes her constant, draining tiredness. Most days she is late for work because she's slow to get moving in the morning. She gets tired very quickly, so she needs to lie down in the middle of the day for about an hour or an hour and a half, to get herself back together again. When she gets home in the evening she's not able for the ordinary run-of-the-mill jobs — organising the household, cleaning, cooking.

Hepatitis C governs what she eats. She can't take red

meat because of the iron content. She can't have kidney, liver or any high-protein foods. Shellfish and prawns are out. Green vegetables are out. Most of the lentils and pulses, such as kidney beans, high in protein, are out.

From behind the screen, the woman explains that her social life is practically non-existent. She's too tired to get dressed up, to go to the theatre or the pictures, to meet friends. She can't drink, and she has to be especially careful in choosing from a menu. In any case, she says, she usually feels too wrecked to do anything except sink into bed.

And there's something else too.

> Q. This is an extremely personal question, but as I say, it is a pertinent question in terms of the Tribunal's understanding of you as a sufferer of this condition. Will you be able to bear more children?
>
> A. No .
>
> Q. Why is that?
>
> A. I had a procedure done about a year and a half ago to stop fertility, in other words I am infertile. I had it done because I felt it would cause. . . . [The woman takes a deep breath, and continues] I did not want to spread hepatitis C. It is that simple.

Making ends meet is a non-stop headache. In her civil service job the woman is classed as 'unestablished'. What it means is that she is unable to gain promotion. She is also not paid for those days when she is sick. In the past twelve months alone she has been absent from work for around three months.

Financial hardship, because of the debilitating effects of hepatitis C, resulted in her losing her home. She is now forced to live in rented accommodation.

When she is asked how she manages, the barely audible reply is:

> I do not, it is as simple as that. I have always to try and make sure that I have reserves in the bank, but if I fall behind, say, with the rent, they are merciless. They expect you to pay one way or another, so you are caught between a rock and a hard place, no matter what.

Beyond the financial strain is the persistent preoccupation about health. Because she has had a kidney transplant she cannot take Interferon for her hepatitis. So she is left facing the progression of the disease without any treatment. And then there is the great fear, shared by others in her situation, that because the hepatitis may affect her immune system, her kidney will reject earlier. 'You will have sleepless nights as a result of that,' she says.

A medical card helps a little, but there was a battle to get it. According to this woman, getting her entitlements involves constant red tape. 'I am fighting with the Health Board all the time,' she says.

The psychological trauma of trying to survive has meant that she needs to see a psychotherapist. But she is also sick with worry about her son, who, she says, needs some form of counselling too.

> He thinks I am going to drop dead on him some morning, which is not the case, but he does not think that he has been told the whole truth and he is quite disturbed about it.

Chapter Three

Valerie's Story

Valerie's old Ford Fiesta is parked in the driveway outside her home. In the window a faded red sticker reads: 'I'm a blood donor.' From when she was seventeen years old, Valerie made regular trips to the Blood Bank. She was even given a silver badge for her efforts. Now, she'll never, ever, give blood again.

In February of 1994, the postman arrived with a letter addressed to her. It was from the Blood Transfusion Service Board. She recognised the familiar envelope. The letter said that there was a problem and invited her to come in for a chat. To her horror, she discovered that she had contracted hepatitis C from a contaminated batch of Anti-D. A liver biopsy confirmed the worst — severe liver damage. Her immediate reaction was one of total shock and disbelief.

> 'Why me?' I kept asking myself. 'Surely, if I have severe damage I would know it.' I was totally unprepared and very, very scared.

Three days after her diagnosis, Valerie began treatment on Interferon. On Mondays, Wednesdays and Fridays, she would get out the kit containing needles, a syringe, alcohol, water and Interferon. Then she would begin injecting herself.

That was scary. I have a total dread of needles. The first time I tried, I bent the needle. My God, I thought, I'll never be able to do this.

For five months Valerie persisted. But the effects of the virus and the side effects of the drug were horrific. She developed mouth ulcers and oral thrush. Her legs became swollen and she began to suffer from arthritis. Most traumatic of all, her hair began to fall out. Sinking back into her chair, she looks back on that summer in 1994.

We went on holiday with the kids. They were expecting us to have a great time, and so we should have. The weather was hot, the spot we'd chosen down in Schull was beautiful, but I felt utterly miserable. I couldn't even talk because of the mouth ulcers, it was just too painful. I felt absolutely humiliated and besides that I was upset because I felt that I was spoiling everyone else's fun. Children expect Mum to be the doer, the one who plans the trips, who picks out the activities for the day, chooses the restaurant. But I was to-tally exhausted, I felt just like a piece of wet rag.

Valerie pauses to take a breath. 'Wait a minute,' she says as she heaves herself up from the chair, and fetches al-bums of photographs from the bookcase. Opening up one of the books, she pulls out snaps of herself, her husband Michael and their three children on happier holidays: Valerie careering down a slide in Trabolgan; Valerie photo-graphed on a hill-walking trip to Gougane Barra; Valerie by the water's edge on a beach in Kerry, dressed in shorts, grinning from ear-to-ear, arms around her two precious daughters.

It's so important for children to have a love of the outdoors, an interest in sports. I was always outside. Now everything has changed. Some days I pull myself around like an eighty-year-old.

After five months on Interferon, Valerie came off the drug

— it simply wasn't working. Then she began to notice that her finger tips would often become icy cold, and so sore that at times she couldn't even hold a knife and fork. There were spots under her nails too, like little thorns. Her haematologist told her that she had something called Cryoglobulinaemia, a fairly rare disorder, but nonetheless, a side effect of hepatitis C.

The medical advice was that she should have treatment to filter her blood and to add new plasma. More blood, she thought with alarm. But there seemed to be no other option. So, every Thursday for a year and a half, Valerie would arrive at Cork University Hospital for the treatment. She dreaded those days. With a doctor and a nurse from the BTSB at hand, a needle was inserted into each of her arms. Then her blood would be filtered out, while new plasma was added, and the process reversed. While all of this was happening, Valerie would lie in bed staring up at the bottle of plasma, at the little drops of blood circulating through her body.

> It was like a nightmare. Here I was again, being given blood from the BTSB. And I knew that it was because of their negligence in the first place that I was here. I couldn't explain how frightened I felt every time I went in. I had a horror of something going wrong. At times I'd try to see the humour of it — 'I hope this lot of blood is better than the batch I got in 1977,' I remember saying once to the nurse.

'Nothing can go wrong,' was the reassuring answer. But it did. During one session Valerie began to feel violently sick. Then she went into spasms. Her husband was horrified — he had no idea what was happening. Her own doctor was called and Valerie was rushed to intensive care, seriously ill. The nightmare was continuing. She had got septicaemia while on the plasma.

Meanwhile, her young daughter waited for Mum to come home. Where was she? She was always back by three o'clock. A neighbour came in to help, and explained to the eleven-year-old what had happened. Valerie didn't finally get home until three weeks later.

> My daughter, was very angry with me during that time. I was always here for her when she came home from school. My husband didn't get back until after ten that night. The children didn't understand why Mum was in hospital and was too sick to come out. I have had to deal with all that anger for a long time afterwards.

Now Valerie is back on Interferon. Last Monday she forgot to inject herself. It was a holiday and there were so many other things to think about. That night she had a massive headache.

'This awful tiredness still amazes and frustrates me,' she says, weary from talking.

> Just look at last Saturday — we decided to have a party, and invited some friends round for cards. I was always such a social animal, the one who would be game for anything. The sun was shining, and I was really looking forward to the night. Then suddenly it was as though someone had turned off a switch, I was no use, my energy levels just packed in. I was determined not to give up the party so our friends came. I planted a smile on my face and pretended that I was grand, but it's very hard trying to retain your sense of humour when you're feeling so shattered. I sat there all night, thinking, 'Will they ever go home?' All I wanted was to crawl into bed. You fight this thing mentally as well as physically. Your mind is active, full of things to do, but your body just isn't able. It's so frustrating.

Having hepatitis C has utterly changed Valerie's life, turned it upside down. 'I'm a totally different person now,' she says. She stops to change her position. Her legs are hurting. There's a chill in the air today and her joints are inflamed.

> I was a free, happy, very contented person who had three children all at school. I had done a Return to Work course —

'Now it's time for me,' I said to myself. We were a great bunch of women on that course. Even when it finished, we stuck together. We would go to the gym, bowling, ballroom dancing — you name it. If the cat had kittens, we'd make a celebration out of it. I was enjoying life. I took a part-time job and was pleased as punch with the money and the freedom. Then this thing hit. Everything changed.

Valerie was forced to give up her job, and to alter her lifestyle completely.

I stopped everything. I can't walk any more — now I'm allowed on my legs for four hours a day. The rest of the time I spend in bed or on this chair.

She turns to look out of the window at the garden, full of bright red geraniums.

I tried to do a bit of gardening yesterday. It's something I really love and the weeds were annoying me, but look how it has left me now. I'm aching all over. I'm like an old fogey.

Some days, especially when it's cold, Valerie stays in bed all day.

I really dread the winters: there's a lot of pain then. But this illness is something that you can't show people. When I'm feeling really horrible and someone says to me, 'Oh you look marvellous', I think to myself, 'I wish I had a broken arm or leg — then they would know that something is wrong.'

I met someone the other day, and I could see her thinking, 'There's really nothing the matter with her.' But when I opened my bag and showed her the medication I'd just got from the chemist — fourteen tablets a day, anti-inflammatories, mouth sprays, saliva replacements, eye drops — I could see her jaw drop. It made her think.

Valerie still cries a lot.

Some days you can just about cope. On others, when you're in a lot of pain, it's difficult. You feel that if you start crying, you'll never stop. But I cry alone.

At times she feels full of guilt. Guilty that she can't spend more time and energy on her children, taking them to Funderland, getting on her bike and riding with them down the narrow country lanes leading to her home. She feels guilty that her hard-working husband has to carry such an added workload. And she cries with frustration because she can't do the everyday things that mums do: helping with the homework, a spot of decorating, spring cleaning the kitchen.

> I have changed from being a happy, healthy person to being an irritable old crock. I think people must be getting fed up with me at this stage.

To help her come to terms with such feelings Valerie has just started one-to-one private counselling. She believes that if she had received proper counselling earlier on, she might now be psychologically further down the road — in a stronger position.

She's angry at the unbelievable insensitivity that she feels was shown by the BTSB.

> At the start we had counselling in the Blood Bank. It was absolutely horrendous. There were two members of the Blood Bank present. I didn't trust them at all, so, as you can imagine, I had no desire to open up. Besides that, I was put with a group of women who were much healthier than I was, who were not on Interferon. I stuck out like a sore thumb.
>
> One woman who had no ill effects turned round to me and said, 'This is all in your mind. I feel perfectly well.' I felt like a hypochondriac. When I came out of that session I cried and cried, I was so upset and humiliated. I was really sick at the time — my hair was falling out, I'd aches and pains, mouth sores — and this woman told me that I was imagining it all.

At four o'clock Valerie collects her youngest daughter from school. Today her knees are stiff. With an effort, she hoists herself up and slowly walks to her car. Pointing to the donor sticker, she shakes her head.

I couldn't tell you how angry I am with the Blood Bank. What they have done to people's lives is like something out of a horror film. They just bungled from one incident to another, not taking responsibility for anything, treating us like test tubes. And they are still bungling — it's amazing. I couldn't live with what they did.

There's something else that worries Valerie too. For three years, she was giving blood which the BTSB knew was infected, but they didn't tell her until 1994.

I didn't know anything about it. I thought I was doing the caring thing. I believed that if anything happened to my children, I could give them blood. Thank goodness it didn't. When I asked what had happened to my blood, the Blood Bank told me, 'Don't worry. If it was donated, it would have been given to someone who was terminally ill. It wouldn't have made any difference.' Imagine being told that.

Chapter Four

Not Just a Woman's Problem

Hepatitis C shows no gender bias. Men have been infected too. No one really knows how many, but it's estimated at around three hundred. Through fear of losing jobs and because of the stigma they believe is associated with hepatitis C, many men live their lives shrouded in secrecy.

John, a man in his fifties, is living a secret hell. He has hepatitis C. No one knows except those in his immediate family. The strain of keeping up a show of normality is immense. John is terrified that he might lose his job, and that people will assume that he contracted the disease through drug abuse or because he was sexually promiscuous. Neither is true.

John's life changed back in 1980 when he had cardiac surgery. At the time he was given multiple blood transfusions. The blood probably saved his life, but it came from an infected batch.

All went well following surgery. John made a very fast and full recovery, and went about the business of getting on with his life. Things were looking good. So grateful was he, in fact, that John regularly gave blood.

Then, in 1993, the bomb-shell hit. He received an ominous letter from the BTSB telling him that there were problems with his last blood donation, and suggesting that he go for testing. John had a PCR test, which was positive, and he was then referred for consultation and a liver biopsy. At that time the biopsy was indecisive. The consultant couldn't get enough tissue to make a complete analysis, so John's blood was monitored for another year. But his liver-function levels, he was told, were 'extraordinarily high'. A second biopsy was called for, and this time severe scarring showed, as well as moderate to severe liver damage. According to John, the onset of cirrhosis of the liver is inevitable.

These days John is on the drug, Interferon. Three times a week, he injects himself. It's not a pleasant experience but he has learned to live with it. What he'll never get used to are the side effects of the drug. He suffers flu-like feelings — aching joints, headaches — and he feels very tired. Despite this, every day he pushes himself to go out to work, keeping his terrible secret to himself. No one at work knows how he is feeling, why he is irritable, why he doesn't talk much when he has down-days. His constant fear is that his illness will be discovered.

> I'm living a surreal existence. Sometimes, for a while, I can forget what's happening, but it always comes back to haunt me, like a constant, nagging worry. No one knows, or must know. There's so much ignorance about hepatitis C. People think that it's the same as AIDS, and if you didn't get it from Anti-D they will jump to all sorts of conclusions.

John doesn't make plans for the future. Before all this happened, he enjoyed life. He was looking forward to retirement, but with hepatitis C he can't think that far ahead. He can't take any long-term loans, make any financial commitments — he may not be there to pay them back. Now, even when he's buying a pair of shoes, John wonders whether he'll be there to wear them out.

Walking used to be something he loved to do. Now that's gone. So has the simple pleasure of going down to the pub for a drink. He feels ill at ease in crowds, opting to stay at home instead.

Something else adds to John's private torment. In 1991 the BTSB knew that his blood was testing abnormal, but they didn't tell him until 1993. All that time, they continued to take blood donations from him.

> I had no knowledge or consent about what was happening. I was left completely in the dark, thinking that my blood donations were being used to save the lives of others. Had I been offered earlier medical treatment would it have made a difference? Would it have delayed the progression of my liver damage?

And the most frightening question of all:

> Where did my infected blood go? Have I unwittingly infected someone else?

The agony of living with such questions, of constantly guarding his secret, is huge. It has caused John grave psychological damage.

He's very angry that proper counselling was not available when he needed it.

> We were hung out to dry. When counselling was arranged, you had no choice of psychiatrist or counsellor. You had to queue up with other patients in a psychiatric hospital.

John felt humiliated, frightened and stigmatised. He has absolutely no faith in assurances from the BTSB or the Health Board about confidentiality either. He feels that despite words to the contrary, a lot of health board employees have access to his files. In the small community in which he lives, that's a big worry.

> The BTSB has shown a total insensitivity towards us. It was bad enough that the state infected us, but the way in which they have treated us was the last straw, the final insult.

*   *   *

Gerry Hogan copes with hepatitis C in a different way. He is able to talk about it. Now he can even see the black humour of his situation. But living with hepatitis C is definitely no joke. Gerry used to love a pint, a smoke and a session at his local, playing the banjo. All that has gone by the board. Now the highlight of the day is climbing into bed.

Gerry's own nightmare started in 1979 when he was riding his motorbike down O'Connell Street, out for the night, minding his own business.

Behind him, two members of a well-known criminal gang thought that he was driving too slowly, so they dragged Gerry off his bike, punched and kicked him to the ground.

> As I began to get up, dazed, I saw two men getting into a car. Full of middle-class outrage, I stood in front of the car to stop it. But the car drove over me, dragging me along for nearly 500 yards. While I was under the car, I could hear them changing gear, and I can remember thinking, 'Someone's trying to kill me.'

A witness later told him that the car was doing 50 miles per hour.

> I was the victim of road-rage before it became fashionable! I was in the wrong place at the wrong time.

When the ambulance arrived, it took him to Jervis Street Hospital, where he was given a blood transfusion. But it was bad blood — plasma from an infected batch.

When he left hospital, Gerry was determined to get back to normal. But things weren't right. He suffered from depression, but put it down to post-traumatic stress. Gradually, over the years, other symptoms appeared. He was constantly exhausted. Sometimes he would experience horrendous hangovers when he'd only had one or two pints.

I believed it was because of the accident. But it didn't go away. I was driving my wife and myself mad, and I was embarrassed because I was always at the doctor's. He would prescribe huge bottles of iron tablets and tell me they would do the trick. Then I went for batteries of tests, for anaemia, brucellosis, allergies, you name it. I was desperate to find out what was wrong with me, to find someone who had the same feeling of absolute exhaustion, so that I could put a name on it. I felt like a total hypochondriac.

In 1994, when the news broke, linking infected blood with Anti-D, Gerry didn't think too much about it. After all, it was a woman's problem. But his mother was getting worried. She heard about contaminated blood from the BTSB and remembered Gerry's transfusion. God forbid that he might be infected with AIDS or something like it.

Her fears were justified. In 1995 he was tested and told that he had hepatitis C.

It was as though I had won the reverse lottery.

His biopsy classed him as 'mild'. One of the nurses even seemed pleased, saying that it could have been more serious. 'Carry on as usual,' was the advice.

Strangely enough, what I felt at first was relief. At last I could put a name on what had been wrong for all those years.

But relief soon turned to anxiety when he was told to be extra careful about personal hygiene, with his toothbrush, his shaving gear. He became sick with worry about his family. Had they been infected?

I was always throwing fits to my kids about using my razors. Sometimes the girls would use them as well as the boys. I was frantic with worry about my children.

Gerry's wife has tested negative but he has decided not to test his children because he is aware that it could blight their lives — questions of insurance, questions of jobs.

The anger and frustration that he felt at first have now subsided a little.

> I really try to live one day at a time.

But days will never, ever, be the same for Gerry, who teaches maths in a Dublin school.

> I have this incredible tiredness all of the time. By afternoons I find even simple maths difficult — you can imagine the ragging I get about that at school from my pupils.

His social life has been devastated. From being an outgoing popular musician, fond of the craic, he now finds it easier to stay at home.

> Going out is too much effort. I don't drink any more and I've lost touch with friends. My hope in finding a cure has also gone by the way — they reckon they will find a cure for AIDS before hepatitis C.

Gerry reckons he's one of the lucky ones.

> There are others worse off than me. I'm fifty and they say it takes thirty years from the onset of infection to premature death. I'll be getting on by then, but that's a death sentence for a younger person. I know many other men and women who are far more serious. And I know that there will be more deaths, horrible deaths like the one Mrs McCole had to suffer.

*   *   *

Not so 'lucky' is William, a young man of twenty-eight. He has had hepatitis C since the age of six, when he received a transfusion of infected blood in Crumlin Children's Hospital. William is married with a young son of sixteen weeks. He is the main breadwinner.

> I had to leave one job. They told me that I was underperforming. Now I work my present job around the hepatitis C, but it's hard — some days I feel so lethargic, I probably only give the work half the effort.

Like John, William has told very few people about his illness.

> I lead a double life. None of my friends or aunts and uncles know that I have hepatitis C. I had a cousin who died of AIDS and I saw the stigma that he had to face.

Life gets harder all the time for William. He's worried about his young family and what will happen to them if he's not around. When he managed to get life insurance, the premium was loaded by 124 per cent because of hepatitis C.

> Sometimes you just want to scream. It's so mentally frustrating. I can't do any of the things I used to.

Playing in a band was a particular passion of his, but that's gone by the way.

> I feel like a 27-year-old man in a 77-year-old body. My mind is razor sharp but I feel as though I'm wearing a lead suit.

On blacker days he thinks about dying.

> I want to live all my life now. I feel as though I'm running out of time.

* * *

Bernard also worries about what will happen to his family. He has chronic liver damage as a result of hepatitis C. Besides having to cope with that, Bernard also battles with Multiple Sclerosis, a disease of the nervous system. He is paralysed from the waist down, and has been confined to a wheelchair since 1984. Before getting hepatitis C, he was trying to live up to the MS motto: 'Make the most of life, the least of MS.' Then, in 1991, he received a blood transfusion — 'Bad blood,' he says, full of anger. From that day on, everything changed.

Bernard remembers being called to the Blood Bank when he was diagnosed in 1995.

I was in this grubby little room with two doctors. 'We have to inform you that you have hepatitis C,' they said. I couldn't believe it. 'Why me?' I kept asking myself. Why have I been dealt such a bad hand?

Things don't look good. Bernard has been told that he is not eligible for a liver transplant and that his life span is between five and eight years.

Imagine the shock of hearing that. Every day, when I wake up, I think, 'Here's another day closer.' My whole personality has changed dramatically. My outlook was always cheerful, but now I'm cranky, bad-tempered. It's difficult to concentrate on anything. For a while my family were saying, 'This isn't my dad.' I had changed so much.

Bernard's wife helps as best she can.

She's a Trojan woman. She talks me through it, but I'm so worried about all my family. I've three sons and I'm a grandfather. They are all still finding it very hard to accept. Adding to his anxiety are worries about insurance, about his mortgage, about what will happen to his family financially.

Because the pressure was so great, Bernard spent some time in a psychiatric hospital.

I just couldn't cope with the fear . . . I still cry. I go down to my room so that I won't upset my family. Sometimes I feel like climbing up the walls, I just can't see any light at the end of the tunnel.

Having MS is very hard, but now I really feel that the life has been knocked out of me. Whatever dignity I had living my life in a wheelchair has been taken away by hepatitis C. The mental torture in unbelievable. I know that there are many men out there who are suffering just like me.

* * *

Some of those who suffer in silence are haemophiliac men. In the Irish Haemophiliac Society, no one who has hepatitis C has been willing to speak publicly. 'Our community has been devastated,' says Rose Daly administrator of the Society.

> There are 500 members in the society and 210 have been infected with the hepatitis C virus from contaminated BTSB products. There have been three deaths to date. And of the 103 members infected with HIV from infected blood products, 59 have died. Some also have hepatitis C. People are very fearful. When I meet members at a funeral I can sense that they are wondering just who will be next.

Some haemophiliac men suffer the agony of being infected with more than one virus. For them, the picture is grim. They can't be treated with the usual hepatitis C drugs. A liver biopsy to establish the extent of the damage is also unlikely as it is regarded as life-threatening for a haemophiliac. Rose Daly believes that the trauma of being infected hits men in different ways from women.

> There is a huge issue of concealment for many of our members. They are terrified that someone will find out. Some men don't even tell their own families, so strong is the fear. Where a man is the main breadwinner they might conceal their condition for fear of losing their job. Not only that, it is impossible for them to get a mortgage or life insurance.

There are many other problems. If men have become unemployed because of hepatitis C, they often seem less able to function in the home setting. After all, their role as breadwinner is gone. If they are feeling sick and fatigued, the tension rises, so their relationships are stressed. Many have a sense of withdrawal, feeling that they have nothing left to offer.

Since alcohol is not advisable, an important part of Irish social life is gone too.

> The male culture often features going out for a pint, meeting other men and talking. Men are often more comfortable in that setting. Now that has been taken away from them.

For younger men, prospects are bleak. There is the prospect of death at an early age. There is also the decision of whether or not to tell a girlfriend that they have been infected. Some have had the painful experience of relationships breaking down when they have told about their infection. In such a situation, marriage prospects are doubtful.

Chapter Five

If I hadn't been born, would you be all right, Mummy?

When Positive Action lobbied the Fine Gael Árd Fheis, children of some of those women who were infected came along with them. They carried posters that read: 'We are to blame.' 'Mum, if you didn't have me, you would not have this?'

One little girl asked her mother in bewilderment: 'If you take water, will it go away?'

The partners, children and parents of those infected suffer with them. They endure the same trauma, bear the same scars. But they are the forgotten ones. Their well of grief, their feelings of anger and of fear, have not been acknowledged. There are no support systems, no counselling facilities available for them. Living with hepatitis C places enormous stress on marriages — some have not survived.

For children, with their youthful idealism, it's especially hard to accept that your mum is tired all the time because someone did this to her. And of course it's hard not to think that if you hadn't been born, it would never have happened.

Kevin was a 1977 baby, the second in a family of four. Because of the infected Anti-D she was given, his mother,

Kathleen, now has severe liver damage with fibrosis. Interferon made things worse, so she had to come off the drug. Now she's living on borrowed time, living out a death sentence. Her family is devastated.

Kevin in particular is finding things hard to accept.

> I was the unlucky one. When I heard on the radio that 1977, my birth date, was the time the infected blood was used, I couldn't stop thinking that my mother's illness was my fault.

Being very close to his Mum, Kevin is terrified that she will die. He has a constant, nagging fear that he will come home one night and she won't be there anymore.

> I don't know what would happen then. Her illness is with me all day, every day. It's always in my mind.

Sharing his feelings could help. But Kevin doesn't talk about his fears to either of his parents. He's frightened that he will upset them and make things worse.

> I'm scared to say what I really feel. The other night I came home after a few pints, and broke down in front of my mother, but then she got really upset, so I won't do it again. When I really feel down, I go to the bottom room in the house and I cry on my own, where no one can hear me.

Unlike his friends, Kevin doesn't play loud music, doesn't shout or make a noise.

> We're all walking on egg-shells. I know my brother and sisters feel hurt and worried too, but we don't talk about it. If anything happened to Mum, I think it would break the whole family apart.

Besides being scared, Kevin also feels anger.

> I'm angry with the Blood Bank. They did this terrible thing to my mum. She did nothing at all to deserve it.

There is confusion too about his mother's medical condition.

I don't really understand what's happening to her body. No one has explained it to me. All I do know is that my mother's liver is slowly rotting away. When I heard about Brigid McCole, that really freaked me.

The unknowing is awful. People think that I'm the funny fellow, the one who makes jokes and laughs, but that's not true. Inside I feel really scared.

Then, lowering his head, he adds:

I've never told this to anyone, but I'm scared that if anything happens, people will turn around and blame me.

*   *   *

Marian's husband, Joe, is someone else who has found the going tough.

I idolise my wife, but our relationship hasn't always been so easy. There have been times when it has been sorely stretched .

For quite some time Joe wondered if his wife loved him at all. Now he understands that what appeared to be indifference was simply the result of ill-health — Marian wasn't falling out of love; she was just plain exhausted.

Marian received Anti-D when their first child, Owen, was born in 1977. After the birth she was tired, but the tiredness didn't go away; instead, it became a part of life. The next twenty years were a chronicle of ill-health, aches and pains — all the things that we now know are commonly associated with hepatitis C.

Joe's life changed. Family outings became the exception rather than the norm. Sometimes Joe and Marian would plan a night out together. A babysitter would be arranged, the restaurant booked. Then, when it came to it, Marian would cry off. There was no explanation.

On top of that, she had become more irritable, snapping at Joe and the children. The sense of humour that had been central to their relationship wasn't so evident. There were tensions on the sexual side of their marriage too.

> It suffered immensely. Now I know that Marian was just exhausted, but then I didn't. I'd be having terrible doubts about the situation, wondering was the relationship all right.

Over the past ten years, Joe has taken charge of most of the housework. He does the hoovering, washes the dishes, and sweeps the floor. He does all the gardening too — something that Marian used to love. The children help too. For as long as they can remember, their mother has always been easily tired, but it's not until they compare her energy levels with those of other mums, or imagine what might have been, that they can see a difference.

When the bombshell hit, and the reason for all those years of ill-health became known, Joe's first reaction was one of relief.

> I was relieved to find that there were reasons, that it wasn't our relationship which was at the root of the problem.

Knowing was one thing, but the knowledge also brought a whole set of new fears for Joe. How long would Marian be around for? Were the children infected?

> We had so many sleepless nights. The massive tension we felt rubbed off onto the children. Our whole family has suffered. My wife's treatment by the Blood Bank was a constant worry too. From day one, I was utterly stunned by their lack of sensitivity. Imagine asking my wife, out loud, if she had other sexual partners, with me, her husband, standing right there, and the whole world listening. On top of that, I didn't trust them. From the very beginning, I felt that they had a certain line to give and stuck to it. The media seemed to know more about what was happening than we did.
>
> For twenty years we have suffered together. Now our relationship is different. It's stronger. But I think a lot of marriages wouldn't have survived. Ours did, thank God.

I'm not a vengeful person — what's gone is gone — but I feel very sad and often angered that so many important times have been forfeited because of someone else's incompetence. You do learn from the downs — you could call it a maturing process — but honestly, what I really feel is that I've just gotten prematurely old.

* * *

'Why hasn't the housework been done?' was one of the things that Michael used to ask when he came home from work. Sometimes he would find his wife, Jean, lying in bed at six o'clock. There would be rows about it. Now the reason for Jean's lethargy is clear. She has severe liver damage, resulting from hepatitis C. Michael is able to smile now about his attitude:

> I always had a difficulty about this house. In my view, it was never clean. I'm a really fastidious person, and, honestly, it used to bother me. I would come home after a long day at work, and the kids' stuff would be all over the place. The kids would often be all over the place too! Homework might not be done. The dinner might not be cooked. It never occurred to me that Jean was exhausted. She was always so very gregarious. I put it all down to her gallivanting or being just too lazy.

Now, in hindsight, Michael feels quite guilty.

> It wasn't the case that she was unwilling — she just wasn't able.

When Jean's symptoms got worse, Michael began to realise that there must be a medical reason for her difficulties at home. Besides that, she didn't seem to have the inclination to drag Michael out any more.

> That's had a huge effect. We used to go out four or five times a week. We'd meet the gang, go for meals, see a play, now

that's finished. Every weekend I'd be out on the golf-course; now, I can't do that any more. There are mornings when Jean literally can't get out of the bed, so I'm needed around here. I've accepted that I have to make changes.

Such changes include doing a lot of work around the house.

I'm doing things I hadn't considered before. For instance, I've had to learn to do the washing without turning everything pink, to tackle the ironing. I've also had to learn about tolerance with my children. That was a failing of mine — I'd come home and all I'd need to do was a bit of Irish homework with them. Jean would have done the rest. Now I'm learning to give them much more attention — to take over from Jean when she's not up to it.

The arguments don't happen now, but Michael feels that that's not always a good thing.

What's happened to Jean has made me unable to argue. We haven't had a good argument for ages. I'm very conscious that if anything is wrong, I hold back from saying it because I don't want to upset Jean — she might not be feeling good. And I know I have to tolerate things I wouldn't dream of accepting before. It involves more sensitivity, but then I'm also putting up with things that I find objectionable. Instead, I see myself bottling things up — that's a problem.

When Jean started on Interferon, Michael also suffered.

Before I walked in the door, she'd turn on me. I know it was because she needed someone to lash out at. She would let fly, and I couldn't say anything back, despite having had an awful day of it myself.

Sometimes he would dread coming home, not knowing what was awaiting him.

I'd be always wondering what I was coming in to — whether Jean had had a reasonable day, or whether she was full of frustration. Then there are times when I'm conscious of Jean holding things back, not wanting to worry me. I resent that — it hurts me, and I feel shut out.

Michael feels huge anger — anger with the BTSB and with the state. For him, one of the ironies of the situation is that he was a blood donor from the age of seventeen, a gold-pin holder. Now he feels betrayed.

> Something that really got to me was, when Jean first started treatment, staff in the BTSB would say to me, 'You're grand; treat it as if things are perfectly normal.' They were denying my right to grieve, making me feel as though I'd no business being angry or having fears. At times, they actually inhibited my ability to express anger.

Despite anger, frustration and resentment, Michael feels that there are some positive sides.

> As a couple we are now much more conscious and much more caring of one another. We enjoy each other's company a lot more because now we are aware of the problems that the other has. It's made me really appreciate Jean, and I believe it's made her appreciate herself too. Since my wife has begun to speak out about what has happened to her, I've noticed a lot of changes. She now realises that she's an important person who has a lot to contribute. I suppose it's made us both more politically conscious.

*   *   *

Women also grieve for loved ones — husbands and fathers — whose lives have been blighted by the suffering and trauma of hepatitis C. Eileen explains softly:

> My father was a simple man, but not a stupid one. All of his life he believed in the system. He had absolute faith in the integrity of those in positions of trust, believing that they were as honest and hardworking as himself. Right up to his death, he spoke of the doctors curing him, of his getting out of hospital so that he could take care of his sick wife. But that wasn't to be. We, his children, watched as this terrible disease slowly took its toll. We saw him struggling to understand what was happening as he became weaker and weaker — finally too weak to carry on.

Eileen's father died on St Patrick's Day, 1997. He died of cirrhosis of the liver, caused by the hepatitis C he had contracted through a transfusion of contaminated blood eight years earlier. He was just a week over seventy years old, but his birthday went by uncelebrated.

Eileen is angry with the system, but not vengeful. What she can never understand is why it happened — why a loving dad and grandad, who had everything to live for, was taken from her because of someone else's carelessness.

> My father deserves answers and explanations. His death lacks the drama of other disasters, and I'm sure that it will soon all be forgotten — left behind as the next scandal takes over. But my family is left with a deep sense of loss and an aching sadness.

*   *   *

Younger men have died too. Joan lost her husband just over a year ago. He was forty-two years old. In 1995 he discovered that he had contracted hepatitis C following a blood transfusion in 1990. Eight years earlier he had had a successful kidney transplant, but it was because of this transplant that his body couldn't accept Interferon, so he just faded away.

> It's all like a bad dream. So unreal. His transplant was working well and he was just getting back on his feet. Things were beginning to work out. Then this terrible blow came.

She and her two teenage boys are finding it difficult to cope.

> Some days I just want to scream. I think I'm going crazy. It's such a bizarre situation.

No one knew about her husband's condition except Joan and the boys.

He felt such a huge stigma about what he described as a 'dirty disease'.

Joan still hasn't told anyone — not even her husband's family. Keeping such a secret to herself adds enormously to the strain. She feels isolated, alone, and utterly bewildered by what has happened. There's a well of anger too.

A terrible wrong has been done, and someone should be punished. What good is compensating people, when my reason for living has gone?

For the sake of her children, Joan will go to the Compensation Tribunal, but she's dreading the thought.

It's hanging over me. No money could bring my husband back. Really it's like handing me thirty pieces of silver.

Chapter Six
Mum's the Word:
Brigid McCole

The McColes come from the tiny mountain village of Loughougher near Dungloe. On the edge of the Atlantic Ocean, it's remote and beautiful — a place of crashing Atlantic rollers, soft pink sunsets. One of the things that Brigid McCole loved best was to take her children for long walks along the beach. Hers was a close and loving family. At the Tribunal of Inquiry, her eldest daughter Bríd, spoke of her mother.

> She was more like a sister to us than a mother because she was always there for us. She was full of life; she would always take part.

Bringing up twelve lively children is hard work at the best of times. But Brigid believed in getting on with life. She never drank or smoked — her pleasure was simply to be with her family.

On 5 November 1977 Brigid McCole was given an injection of Anti-D. She believed that it would save the life of her baby. Eighteen years later, it was the cause of her own death.

The family's first sign of their mother's illness was about ten years ago. She became very fatigued; her bones were sore. Then she developed clots on her leg and on her lung. Tests were done, but no one could discover why she

was so ill. The nearest GP was fourteen miles away, and
Brigid hated to bother him.

> She would be sick and she would never ever want to put
> you to any trouble or anything like that.

Bríd recalls one particular night when her mother was in
great pain.

> We were at a loss. We could not do anything for her. But this
> night we called the doctor out. It was a locum, someone who
> was standing in for our GP, and he actually called two of my
> sisters out of the room and he said to them, 'Do you think that
> it is all in her mind? Do you think that she is imagining it?'

Things didn't improve. Brigid McCole herself began to
wonder whether it was all in her mind. There was no
counselling, no one to help her. She felt alone and isolated. Over the years there were more blood tests, more
visits to doctors, but no one had the answer.

When a test for hepatitis C finally became available,
Brigid knew for sure that the sickness wasn't in her mind.
The diagnosis of hepatitis C left the family bewildered.
They knew nothing about this strange disease. As they
lay in their beds at night, listening to their mother scream
with pain, they felt utterly impotent, completely at a loss
as to how to help her.

Once a month, Brigid went down to a Dublin hospital
for treatment. It was an exhausting journey that took nine
hours. Beginning at six o'clock in the morning, she would
take a taxi to Letterkenny, and then pick up the hospital
bus. It was a long, tedious journey to Beaumont hospital.
the bus would stop off along the way to pick up patients,
and then drop them off at other hospitals. When she
eventually arrived, she would spend a week in Beaumont. It was a very lonely time. Dublin was a long way
from home, and as the McColes had no family living
nearby, there was no one to visit her. In the beginning,

there were no phonecalls either — the family didn't have a telephone. If they wanted to speak to their mother, they would have to make the long trek down.

In November 1994, Brigid McCole, together with other women from Positive Action, were invited to meet President Robinson at Áras an Uachtaráin.

A photograph of Mrs McCole greeting the President was among her most treasured possessions, and she always carried it in her handbag.

It was a welcome show of solidarity from a woman of importance. While the President was powerless to change anything, her willingness to meet the women was in marked contrast to the apparent indifference that they felt was coming from the government.

Minister Michael Noonan set up the compensation tribunal in September 1995 and urged women to attend, but Brigid wasn't interested. She believed that the only way she would get at the truth was to go to the High Court.

Brigid Ellen McCole vs. *the BTSB, the State and the National Drugs Advisory Board* was the first High Court challenge to be taken by a hepatitis C victim. But the state and the various state agencies made it quite clear that they were going to make it as long and difficult as possible.

Their first swipe at Mrs McCole was to deny her the anonymity that she sought. Her legal team pointed out that many victims of hepatitis C had been subjected to 'invidious discrimination', and that Brigid's family, and she herself, had felt socially ostracised within the community. The state stood firm, insisting that she couldn't take her case as Brigid Roe, but must use her own name.

When that didn't stop her, they said that Mrs McCole had left the challenge too late. Since she had been infected in 1977, the state lawyers argued, the time to sue had run out. Such a claim seemed unbelievable, since none of the victims, including Brigid McCole, had even heard of

hepatitis C until 1994. They even questioned whether the
BTSB had manufactured and supplied Anti-D at all,
whether Mrs McCole had received it in the first place.

Pressure continued. The time for lodging compensation claims was running out, and the Minister refused to
extend it. If Mrs McCole didn't settle by the end of June
1996, she and her family could end up with virtually
nothing.

Meanwhile, her health deteriorated. She was in pain
practically all the time. Her daughter, Bríd, later told the
Tribunal of Inquiry:

> At nights you'd hear her scream out in pain.

It became clear that Brigid might die before her case could
be heard on 8 October. Her medical consultant confirmed
this view, and in the summer of 1996 her legal team,
headed by John Rogers SC, asked for an earlier hearing. It
was refused, adding yet another burden to the huge
physical and emotional stress that Mrs McCole was
forced to suffer.

There were other pressures too. Earlier on in the year,
the BTSB had lodged £175,000 in court, which Mrs
McCole could accept if she chose. This meant that even if
she proceeded with the court case and won, if the award
was less than that amount, she would be liable for legal
costs for the BTSB from the date of the lodgement. It was
becoming like a deadly game of poker.

The full weight of the state was being pitted against
one terminally ill woman. Mrs McCole, now in a critical
condition, was transferred to the liver unit at St Vincent's
Hospital. She agonised about what she should do, what
would happen to her family if she had to pay costs. There
seemed to be no way out of it.

Then, on 20 September 1996, there was a totally
unexpected turnabout. Her senior counsel came to visit

her with a letter from the BTSB solicitors. The letter admitted liability and offered her an unreserved apology for her illness. It read:

> Our preparations for the trial of this action have now reached a stage at which together with counsel and our client, we can take a considered view on the issue of negligence in light of the facts and allegations in this case.
>
> With counsel, we have undertaken an extensive review of these facts which go back 25 years. The various allegations made in the proceedings have been put to such witnesses as are alive and as are available to give evidence. A range of experts at home and abroad also have been consulted. On consideration of this extensive review and following legal advice, our client has decided to admit liability to your client in relation to her claim for compensatory damages for negligence.
>
> In arriving at this decision, our client has taken into account the evidence and guidance available to it. Our client has also been very concerned to ensure that your client should not suffer by having to participate in a trial in which negligence is an issue.
>
> This admission is solely for the purposes of these proceedings and in the context of the facts and circumstances relating to your client only. Our client is prepared to compensate your client in full for pain and suffering, loss and damage suffered by her as a result of the injuries caused by our client's negligence. Our client will also pay any costs to which your client may be entitled, to be taxed in default of agreement on a party and party basis. We have been instructed that our client is in a position to meet and satisfy all such compensatory damages, together with any costs that might be due to your client. . . .

Liability had, at last, been admitted. An apology was offered. However, there was a final sting in the tail. The letter went on:

> If your client should discontinue the claim for aggravated and exemplary/punitive damages against our client, our client will not seek payment of any costs attributable to this

issue. We hope that this proposal will mean the speedy and simplified resolution of the issues in these proceedings.

However it is important to set out the position that our client will be reluctantly obliged to adopt should you reject these proposals. If your client proceeds with her claim against the NDAB and the State defendants, our client will seek all additional costs thereby incurred from the date hereof and this letter will be used in support of such application to the court.

Similarly, if your client proceeds with her claim for aggravated and exemplary/punitive damages against our client and fails, then our client will rely on this letter in an application to the court against your client for all costs relating to the claim for such damages and for an order setting off any such costs in favour of our client against any costs to which your client might otherwise be entitled. . . .

In other words, although the BTSB had now accepted liability, if Mrs McCole didn't accept the compensation offer, she and her family could still be left penniless and destitute should she lose her case. Reluctantly, she decided to settle.

It was a hard decision to make. On the one hand, Brigid McCole felt a strong, burning obligation to pursue the truth for the sake of all victims. On the other hand, there was her family to think of. There seemed to be no option. She accepted the sum of £175,000 compensation. Twelve days after she had signed the agreement, Brigid McCole died.

Bríd McCole, who had been constantly at her mother's side, later described just how terrified and intimidated her mother had felt during those last few days.

> Why were they threatening her like this? I can never forgive them. She suffered so much. It was something that should never have happened. The suffering and pain she went through was just inhuman.

On 5 October, Brigid McCole's body was removed from her home to St Patrick's Chapel, Meenaweal, Gweedore, where a funeral mass took place. Later in the afternoon, she was buried at Magheragallan Cemetery in a grave that she had chosen herself. Hundreds of people thronged to her home to pay their respects to her twelve heart-broken children, and to her husband, Brian.

Brigid Ellen McCole's battle, fought so courageously, was simply to uncover the truth. Why, she wanted to know, had she been forced to suffer so much, and who was to blame? The response of the state was a combina-tion of tough legal moves and what seemed to the McCole family and many others like constant harass-ment. By fighting her every step of the way, it seemed that the state was hoping that the fifty-four-year-old Donegal mother would eventually tire of the battle and settle quietly for compensation, thus keeping the lid on the whole affair. But the state had reckoned wrongly. Money was the last thing that motivated Mrs McCole. What she and her family wanted was justice.

Nothing can bring Mrs McCole back, or take away the huge loss felt by her family. But her death was not in vain. The courage and determination that she showed, despite being terminally ill, had huge ramifications, which will live long after her, and which led directly to the establishment of the Tribunal of Inquiry.

One of the bombshells that emerged during the course of her High Court case was the discovery of a 'missing file'. In searching for all relevant material, Mrs McCole's lawyers uncovered the famous file among other material held by the BTSB.

While the Tribunal of Inquiry concluded that the file 'did not constitute any fundamental difference in informa-tion available', the file did prove categorically that in 1976–77 the BTSB had knowledge that Patient X had 'infectious hepatitis', rather than jaundice as had previously been claimed. The importance of this discovery was that the information had not been available to Miriam Hederman-O'Brien's Expert Group when it had made its report in January 1995. The *Expert Group Report* had found the source of infection to be a donor with jaundice of 'unknown origin'. The Group had made a report without having access to all the facts. Opposition parties in the Dáil went to town on the discovery. Fianna Fáil TD Máire Geoghegan-Quinn questioned the accountability of a state agency, adding that the scandal had gone on for too long. Liz O'Donnell of the PDs wanted to know why such a crucial file was not given to a government group set up to investigate the whole hepatitis C affair. In response, Minister Noonan said he had not seen the file at all.

Positive Action called for a full judicial investigation into the whole scandal.

On 8 October, just six days after Brigid McCole's death, her court case was due to begin. The hearing lasted a mere six minutes. Members of her family packed the courtroom and heard the BTSB apologise for the illness and distress which she had suffered, through their actions. But for Bríd McCole and her brothers and sisters, the apology rang hollow. In a statement they said:

> Though our mother is not with us today we know in our hearts that she is finally at peace and would be happy that the powers that be have finally admitted to what she always knew to be their fault.
>
> It would have been easier for our mother to accept the rulings of the Tribunal. However, all she really ever wanted was a public acknowledgement that a wrong had been done. As it turned out, that decision resulted in a very difficult year for her. Despite the pain and hardship of travelling to Dublin for treatment, she never once faltered in her determination to have the truth told.
>
> In the end she was never allowed to state her case. Throughout her life our mother always put the family first and only in her final hours did she finally submit to putting her name to a paper in order that, once again, she would be

taking care of us to the best of her ability.

In our hearts our mother is forever young and will be sadly missed not only by her mother, husband, brothers, sons and daughters, but also the grandchildren that she will never get the chance to enjoy.

The Blood Bank went on to apologise 'sincerely to every person infected by hepatitis C through the BTSB's blood and blood products and to their families and friends', concluding:

The BTSB and its current new management have worked and will continue to work to ensure that there will never be a repeat of this tragedy, which has affected so many innocent persons.

Such sentiments failed to impress the McCole family and members of Positive Action. What they wanted was the whole truth — the truth that could only be made known by a judicial inquiry.

That same day, the McColes sent a letter to Minister Noonan, demanding answers to five key questions concerning their mother, which remained unanswered:

1. Why did the Blood Transfusion Service Board use plasma from a patient undergoing therapeutic plasma exchange when it was unsafe to do so?

2. Why did the Blood Transfusion Service Board ignore the ample warnings of jaundice, hepatitis and adverse reactions to Anti-D in 1977 and again take no steps when they were informed of the infection of Anti-D with hepatitis C on 16 December 1991?

3. Why did the Blood Transfusion Service Board not inform the infected women in 1991 and why did they not report the infection to the Department of Health as they were obliged by law to do?

4. Why was the Blood Transfusion Service Board permitted to manufacture Anti-D unlawfully and without licence under the Therapeutic Substances Act, 1932, from 1970 to 1984?

5. In their letter of 20 September 1996, the Blood Transfusion Service Board did two things: they admitted liability and apologised, but only in the context of a threat that were she to proceed with a case for aggravated/exemplary damages, and not to succeed, they would pursue her for costs. What was the justification for this threat?

Once again the government was in the hot seat. In a special Dáil debate, Minister for Health Noonan was pilloried by opposition deputies.

Liz O'Donnell claimed that there had been a 'cover up of facts' from the very beginning. She made no distinction between state liability and BTSB liability, and said that the Minister was attempting to distance the state from the BTSB.

> I believe that this is a masterpiece of political fiction. It is a nonsense, the Blood Board is the state.

She further added:

> [The] debate has highlighted the impotence of Dáil Éireann as a body which holds the executive to account.

Fianna Fáil's Máire Geoghegan-Quinn spoke of a state board 'bordering on the criminally negligent', and of a 'massive cover-up'.

Positive Action repeated its demand for a Tribunal of Inquiry, arguing that this was the only way that the truth would emerge.

Following Mrs McCole's death, and the revelations of the 'missing file', there seemed no other option. The government announced that the long-fought-for Tribunal would take place.

The McColes' first four questions, concerning the behaviour of the BTSB between 1977 and 1991 were to be included in the terms of reference. The fifth question, concerning the behaviour of the state, was judged by the Tribunal to be outside its terms of reference.

But the story hadn't ended. Why had the state treated Mrs McCole with such hostility? To what extent were Minister Noonan and the government responsible? Such pertinent questions would resurface later.

In tears, Bríd McCole gave evidence about her mother at the Tribunal of Inquiry.

> I feel very strongly that only that my mother died this tribunal would not have come through. It is only a shame that someone had to die for this to happen.

Brigid McCole's story raises serious questions about the nature of our democracy. In theory, we elect a government to represent us and offer us protection. Yet Brigid McCole found that far from being her protector, the state became her enemy. An individual who had been grossly wronged by one arm of the state was immediately forced into a confrontational situation. And instead of making restitution to a dying woman, the state fought her every inch of the way.

As if nothing had been learned, Brigid McCole's aggressive legal treatment was later to be repeated in the case of a Co. Carlow woman, Mary Quinlan, who, like Mrs McCole, was motivated by a powerful sense of justice. The similarities between the experiences of the two women are striking. Both have large families — Mrs Quinlan has eight children. Like Mrs McCole, she was infected with hepatitis C through contaminated Anti-D administered in 1977. Both opted to go the High Court route, beginning their actions around the same time in 1995.

Like Mrs McCole, Mrs Quinlan was denied the anonymity that she sought, and was left waiting for a considerable period for her case to be heard, despite being seriously ill. There was also huge difficulty in getting medical information. It took an incredible forty requests in court for her finally to obtain her medical records from the BTSB.

Most alarming of all was that only weeks before her scheduled High Court hearing of 2 July 1997, she received letters from the state's legal team, warning her that she could be liable for huge legal costs. It was a tactic that had incensed the McCole family and the public in general.

In April 1997, in a letter to then Minister of Health, Michael Noonan, she wrote:

> Is it government policy to make the rest of my life, or anyone taking similar court action, as difficult as possible?

In the end, Mrs Quinlan settled her two-year legal action, for an undisclosed amount, just minutes before it was due to be heard in the High Court. Commenting afterwards, a weary Mrs Quinlan said that the state 'had not spared [her] anything', and that despite public outrage at the treatment of Brigid McCole, she would not encourage anyone to go through the experience of taking an action through the High Court. She continued:

> All political parties bear a responsibility to ensure that, if something like this ever happens again, the State or its agencies will not threaten huge court costs and legal technicalities to stop its citizens going to court for their rights.

Chapter Seven
Betrayal of Trust

How did an organisation that was widely respected, absolutely trusted, and regarded as a pillar of the state degenerate into disrepute and disgrace? Why did those in positions of responsibility and power betray public trust, and disregard even the most basic standards of safety and care? Why were the 'wrongful acts', 'failures' and 'inadequacies' described in the *Tribunal of Inquiry Report* allowed to go unchecked for twenty years?

The catalogue of events beginning in 1976 has left a trail of human misery. It is a medical mystery story that makes for chilling reading — a story with unhappy endings, in which the BTSB is the main player.

Set up in 1948, the BTSB was a source of immense public pride. Solid and reliable was the image generated in the public mind. When, in 1970, a unit was set up for the production of Anti-D from the plasma of Irish donors exclusively, the move was applauded. It was a significant achievement for national director Dr Jack O'Riordan and his colleagues. Here at last, it was proudly said, was a home-spun product. There would be no more need for imports from abroad. However, for this home product to run short at any time, or to be replaced by imported Anti-D, would have meant a major admission of failure — in the eyes of the BTSB, that is.

Assisting the BTSB in the setting up of the unit was a

pioneer of the process, Professor Hans Hoppe, from the Central Institute for Blood Transfusion in Hamburg. As one of the first witnesses at the Tribunal of Inquiry, Professor Hoppe gave evidence that in 1972 he had advised the BTSB that he had advanced the process of extracting Anti-D by abandoning a particular manufacturing step and introducing a new filtration method. He had also recommended that any donation for making Anti-D should be quarantined by the BTSB for six months, during which time the donor should be repeatedly tested.

For some reason the BTSB decided to stay with the original method and not take on the Hoppe modification. As Senior Counsel James Nugent later told the Tribunal of Inquiry, the Blood Bank, in effect, 'abandoned the instructor and chose to fly solo'.

Patient X

The story begins in the autumn of 1976 when a pregnant woman (now known as Patient X) went into Our Lady's Hospital for Sick Children, Crumlin. She had a history of Rhesus Haemolytic disease and had had a number of births which had been severely affected by it. So, to save the child she was bearing, she underwent a course of plasma-exchange treatment. It would help prevent her from giving birth to a 'blue baby'. The course continued for twenty-five weeks.

During her treatment, the BTSB made a discovery — the woman was an unusually rich source for making Anti-D serum. So delighted were staff at the BTSB that they began producing the product from her plasma. But in the rush to reap the plasma, they neglected to ask for the patient's consent. Patient X knew nothing about it, and neither did her consultant. In fact, she has said that she would never have given consent to the procedure, because earlier in her life she had been infected with tuberculosis.

Patient X became jaundiced, and for a while the BTSB stopped using her blood. But then, when she seemed to have recovered, they began again. Testing was carried out to see whether the plasma was still suitable to manufacture Anti-D. Ten separate forms circulated between Crumlin Hospital and the BTSB. Each had the words INFECTIVE HEPATITIS written on them.

By the end of that year, Dr Jack O'Riordan, National Director of the BTSB, and Dr J.L. Wilkinson and Dr Terry Walsh, senior medical staff, were all aware that Patient X had Infective Hepatitis and a display of jaundice.

> It cannot therefore be doubted that by the middle of December 1976, the entire senior medical staff concerned for the BTSB with this question of the plasma obtained from patient X, that is to say, Dr O'Riordan, Dr Wilkinson and Dr Terry Walsh, were all aware of a diagnosis of infective hepatitis and the display of jaundice by the patient (*Tribunal of Inquiry Report*, p. 19).

Unbelievably, despite having possession of such crucial information, the BTSB kept quiet — failing to report such knowledge to anyone. Further supplies of plasma were taken from Patient X and used to manufacture Anti-D. Between 14 February 1977 and 4 July 1977, a total of sixteen batches of Anti-D were made. Eight of these batches, when tested later, were found to be infected with hepatitis C. The number of doses per batch varied from 250 to 400. Among these was batch number 250, the one given to Brigid McCole — the one that ultimately killed her.

Apart from a serious breach of ethical conduct in not telling Patient X that her blood was being used, four other most basic principles of the medical profession were ignored — principles that had nothing to do with bureaucratic red tape, but concerned implications for human life:

> • It is a fundamental principle of the indications for rejection of a donor of blood that a person with a history of

viral hepatitis or jaundice of unknown origin, shall be excluded permanently as a blood donor....

- A period of at least six months should elapse from the date of the last infusion or injection of blood before a person receiving a transfusion of blood or blood components is accepted as a donor....

- An abnormal reaction to the injection of blood or a blood product should be reported to the National Drugs Advisory Board....

- It was a fundamental principle of blood transfusion and the preparation of blood products that should any question be raised of any substance concerning the safety of a product, even without convincing proof of infection, it should be totally recalled and supplies of it destroyed (*Tribunal of Inquiry Report*, pp. 21, 22).

More Damning Evidence

In July 1977, the Rotunda Hospital notified the BTSB of three patients who were showing hepatitis-like symptoms. All three had received doses of Anti-D manufactured from batch 238, one of the batches manufactured using Patient X's plasma. GPs attending the three women confirmed to the BTSB that they believed the hepatitis might be associated with doses of Anti-D. The link was established.

How did the BTSB react to such vital information? One would have expected the Board to act immediately to withdraw and destroy all batches of Anti-D made from Patient X's plasma. Instead, the amazing decision was to stop using her plasma to make Anti-D, but to continue using those stocks already held.

Stocks Already Held

Cecily Cunningham was the principal biochemist in charge of the laboratory where the Anti-D was manufactured. She said that said that on 25 July, she received an instruction not to use Patient X's plasma in any more donor pools, but she received no instruction as to what she was to do with batches already manufactured. She continued to use them.

> Mrs Cunningham does not bear as great a responsibility for the contamination of the blood supply with hepatitis C derived from the incident of Patient X as do the medical staff at that time employed by the BTSB. She does however bear an important and serious responsibility nonetheless. Once the instruction had been given to her in one instance to hold for a period the plasma derived from Patient X and in the other instance to discontinue the making of Anti-D from it, having regard to her qualifications and experience, she clearly owed a duty to have these two matters clarified if she did not understand the reasons for them, and should have insisted, as far as was within her power to do so, that no further batches of Anti-D so made should be issued or made available (*Tribunal of Inquiry Report*, p. 28).

Two years earlier, in 1975, an incident had occurred in the laboratories of the BTSB, which also involved Mrs Cunningham. When a freezer used for storing Anti-D in the fractionation laboratory had broken down, she had placed the Anti-D for storage in a freezer situated in the microbiology laboratory — a separate laboratory in which doses of reagents containing active virus for testing against hepatitis B were already placed. While the Tribunal found that this incident was not responsible for the infection of the Anti-D supplies with hepatitis C, the report stated:

> It is quite clear that this was an extremely serious breach of what should have been a fundamental distinction between the sterile laboratory, such as the Anti-D laboratory where blood products were manufactured and stored, and the laboratory which stored what would be the contaminating agents such as reagents for the testing against viruses . . . it constitutes a serious breach of safety precautions by Mrs Cunningham and, on her evidence that her action in retaining it and reissuing it was approved by the medical staff, a serious breach by them of the standards which they should have applied (*Tribunal of Inquiry Report*, pp. 28–9).

Between August and December 1977, four more women who had received Anti-D from batches contributed to by Patient X were reported by their GPs as having suffered from hepatitis and jaundice. Still there was no recall by the BTSB of batches that had already been issued — despite the fact that a scientific committee comprising Dr O'Riordan, Dr Walsh, Cecily Cunningham and other senior officers was meeting weekly to discuss relevant issues, issues that must have included Patient X and links with hepatitis through the administration of Anti-D.

> ... it is clear that the question of the plasma obtained from Patient X, the condition of jaundice and Hepatitis reported with regard to Patient X and the complaints of the recipients of Anti-D from batches donated in part by Patient X who had developed Hepatitis after being dosed with the Anti-D, were all matters discussed on a number of occasions at meetings of the Scientific Committee during the year 1977 and in particular, it would appear, from July 1977 (*Tribunal of Inquiry Report*, p. 21).

Meanwhile, specimens of blood from the women in the Rotunda Hospital had been sent to the Middlesex Hospital for further testing. Results were inconclusive and the doctors in the UK decided to freeze the samples until better technology became available. A letter sent in September 1977 from Dr Dane of the Middlesex Hospital to Dr O'Riordan of the BTSB described what had happened since Patient X first became jaundiced in 1976 as a 'mystery'. Dr Dane's words cast doubt on the safety of using the plasma to make Anti-D.

At the Tribunal of Inquiry Dr Dane spoke of the BTSB's decision to continue issuing Anti-D made from Patient X's plasma

> I can't explain it at all. I do not know what was going on in their minds to make them do this.

He did not think that it was 'any secret the donor

(Patient X) had jaundice'. The specimens were 'obviously jaundiced', with a 'greenish tinge'.

On 2 September 1977, Dr Dane wrote to Dr Jack O'Riordan (Chief Medical Consultant of the BTSB), informing him that Patient X had tested negative for hepatitis B, but that he was retaining samples for further tests, which might 'solve the mystery'.

Belief at that time was that viruses were not transmitted through Anti-D, but there was no scientific evidence to back this up.

'Whatever the belief was it was not the scientific practice to use plasma from a patient with jaundice,' said Dr Dane. At the Middlesex Hospital he pointed out that they would normally discard everything six months back, at least, where there were any suspicions.

It was certainly not safe to use plasma from Patient X, even though it had been cleared of having hepatitis B. Dr Dane told the Tribunal of Inquiry that the plasma 'should have been withdrawn immediately the association was made'. 'The problem could have been easily controlled if people had wanted to do it,' he added.

According to Dr Dane, the seven cases notified to the BTSB between August and December 1977 would have been 'more than enough' to put a hold on everything. 'The first three specimens were enough.' Dr Dane also considered it 'extraordinary' that Patient X was used as a source for plasma as she had received multiple transfusions. This meant that the risk of her having infective hepatitis increased 'one hundredfold'.

The bad blood taken from Patient X began to circulate, in Anti-D and in blood transfusions. Most chilling of all was the fact that many of the women who were infected with hepatitis C subsequently went on to donate blood — donations given to a trusted organisation in the hope that they might help to save life.

Patient Y: The Nightmare Continues

Patient Y started plasma exchange treatment in St James's Hospital in August 1989. Ten donations of blood were made by her. A month later, she became infected with hepatitis C from contaminated plasma she herself had received from the BTSB. After she became infected, the BTSB took twelve more donations from her and froze them for later use.

In January 1991, Cecily Cunningham decided to use some of this frozen plasma to make more Anti-D. She asked Terry Walsh, one of the boards medical consultants, to have the patient tested for HIV and Hepatitis B.

But Cecily Cunningham, although she had twice asked Dr Walsh for tests, did not wait until the tests were done. Incredibly, she went ahead and used the plasma to make Anti-D. She later told the Tribunal of Inquiry:

> We were a bit short of Anti-D. I just ploughed on.

Nine batches were issued without the donor having been tested.

In October 1991 a specific test for hepatitis C became available. Two tests on Patient Y's blood were taken. Both showed positive for hepatitis C. Then, in July 1992, when two further tests were taken, the same result showed — positive for hepatitis C. The course of action was clear. According to the Board's own standard operating procedure, the donation should be withdrawn from stock, discarded and destroyed.

Instead, the BTSB continued to use Patient Y's plasma to make Anti-D. Right up to 1994, it was still being issued. As a result, forty-three people were infected with the hepatitis C virus, and another thirty to forty have hepatitis C antibodies in their bloodstream.

Patient Y herself did not find out until 1996 that she had hepatitis C.

Letter from Middlesex Hospital (16 December 1991)

In August 1991, the Middlesex Hospital asked permission from the BTSB to test the samples of plasma that they had kept from 1977. Then, on 16 December 1991, a letter containing crucial information was faxed from the Middlesex to Dr Terry Walsh, Chief Medical Consultant. It strongly suggested that contaminated Anti-D was responsible for the outbreaks of hepatitis C in 1977 — a bombshell that needed to be acted upon immediately.

Cecily Cunningham was aware of the contents of the letter. Another member of the BTSB, Dr Emer Lawlor, a consultant haematologist was told of the fax. Dr Lawlor realised that there was a problem and that many more women might be affected. Dr Walsh said that he would come back to her, and that they would 'sit down and discuss it'. But, amazingly, he didn't. There was absolutely no response from him. Christmas came, and nothing happened. In her evidence to the Tribunal of Inquiry, Dr Lawlor said that she had been busy:

> He (Dr Walsh) never came back to me and I forgot all about it. It just totally slipped my memory.

This failure to do anything meant that others were infected. As Dr Lawlor later stated in her evidence, 'About 30 people wouldn't have got the hepatitis C virus had the fax been acted upon.

> It is quite clear that the response of the BTSB to this letter of December 16 was non-existent and totally and completely inadequate. It is equally clear that the consequence for the blood supply and blood products of this inadequacy was that a procedure for testing recipients of Anti-D derived from plasma manufactured in the years 1976 and 1977 could have been initiated two years before it was, and that upon the necessary result of such screening, namely information concerning the further donations by such recipients of blood to the blood transfusion service, that there could have been a

large-scale recall of products two years before that became possible and by these and other steps much infection of recipients of blood and blood products with Hepatitis C would have been avoided.

In addition, recipients of infected blood and blood products could have been diagnosed and treated two years earlier than they were (*Tribunal of Inquiry Report*, p. 59).

It would appear that the reason why the reaction was nonexistent was a total refusal to face the consequences of what had been done in regard to Patient X in 1976/1977 (*Tribunal of Inquiry Report*, p. 149).

Whilst at the Tribunal Dr Lawlor had expressed deep regret, the *Tribunal Report* found that 'it would be unreal, and therefore unjust to impose upon Dr Lawlor, in respect of this incident, any responsibility' (*Tribunal of Inquiry Report*, p. 60).

Chapter Eight
Crisis Management

On Monday, 21 February 1994, the press were called to Pelican House and the hepatitis C story broke. At a press conference in Mespil Road, a large group of reporters sat in stunned silence as they listened to Dr Joan Power and her colleagues — Chief Medical Consultant Dr Terry Walsh and the BTSB Chief Executive Ted Keyes — read from the nine-page prepared press release:

> It is on foot of Dr Power's investigations that the board has decided to institute a nationwide testing service for all RH negative women who were administered with Anti-D
>
> The BTSB wants to allay public concern that there is a widespread problem. The chief medical consultant believes that the best form of assurance women can be given is to provide blood testing for all those who may be concerned.

This was the biggest health crisis in the history of the state. The sheer scale of the problem was daunting — over 65,000 women needed to be tested — the first mass screening for hepatitis C in the world. The news brought shock and horror to families all over Ireland.

So how did the BTSB manage a crisis of such magnitude? Did the Board have an emergency strategy that could put in place quickly and efficiently? After all, similar problems had arisen in the 1980s in relation to HIV — particularly with regard to haemophiliacs. And in any case, Joan Power's research, which had begun in 1991, had been pointing in the direction of a problem for some time.

It became clear very quickly that there was no emergency plan; on the contrary, chaos ensued. The Department of Health was informed only a few days before the public announcement, and its response was far from adequate. Instead of foresight and planning, it seemed to react in a piecemeal, fragmented way as the crisis unfolded. Management was left largely in the hands of those who had caused the problem — the BTSB.

One of the most urgent priorities for the Blood Bank was the recall of existing stocks of Anti-D. To prevent further tragedy it was essential that all infected doses were accounted for and immediately withdrawn.

But the reaction of the Blood Bank fell dismally short of what was expected. Unbelievably, the system of recall consisted merely of a telephone call from the Chief Medical Consultant, Dr Walsh, very often to one individual working in a large institution. This was then followed by a letter. But such a hit-and-miss approach wasn't good enough, as the Tribunal of Inquiry later stated:

> The proper standard to be applied to any recall procedure in the circumstances which became known in February 1994 was to assume any dose issued could be lethal in the sense that it could cause wholly unnecessary, very serious and potentially fatal disease (*Tribunal of Inquiry Report*, p. 66).

As the BTSB knew of the number of institutions and individuals who held stocks of Anti-D, securing them was not such a difficult job. As the Report stated, the Blood Bank

> should have physically collected the Anti-D, and then put into place the checking of the doses taken back against all stocks outstanding, ensuring that all issued stocks had effectively been recalled (*Tribunal of Inquiry Report*, p. 67).

But apparently the BTSB didn't see the need to take such extra precautions. All stocks were not accounted for. It appeared that nine 'potentially fatal' doses were administered after the recall.

One of these was at a nursing home in Limerick, managed by Sr Ann Kelleher. She told the Tribunal of Inquiry that the BTSB made no telephone call at all before April 1994, and that no letter was ever sent. By the time the phone call was made, the stocks of Anti-D which were in the nursing home had innocently been used.

Another priority for the BTSB was the replacement of the home-produced Anti-D with an imported product. But here again, ensuring absolute public safety does not appear to have been uppermost in BTSB thinking. Two serious licensing breaches of safety occurred.

The first was on 17/18 February when the BTSB informed the Department of Health that the Canadian-imported replacement product had been licensed by the Federal Drugs Association in the United States. This was not true. The product was not, in fact, licensed by the FDA until April of that year. The second breach was that, at the time it was imported, the product had not been approved by the Licensing Authority in Ireland either.

This situation was accidentally discovered by Senator Mary Henry who was making separate enquiries. Once again, the BTSB approach to management and to safety was in question. Whilst there was a clear need for a substitute product, was an unlicensed product not a 'potentially fatal' one.

After the recall of the contaminated product, the second most urgent issue was testing. Again, the BTSB and the Department of Health seemed ill-prepared for the exhaustive testing programme that was clearly required.

For instance, when the news became public, many GPs were inundated with anguished calls. Dr Michael Dunne GP, then Chairman of the Irish Council of General Practitioners, felt strongly that the situation was not handled properly:

> There was no logical thinking in how the situation was han-
> dled. It was clear that GPs would be flooded with enquiries —
> just as we had been during a previous Rubella scare which
> followed a programme on the Gay Byrne Show. Many GPs
> were extremely annoyed that they were not informed before-
> hand. After all, a doctor needs to provide factual high-grade
> information to patients.

The Tribunal found that, on balance, the decision to delay informing the GPs was not unreasonable, given the possibility of rumours leaking out before the press conference. However, since GPs are always in the front-line many found it difficult to understand why they were not informed in the week preceding the crisis. Most GPs heard about the situation only through the announcement on national media.

For those who did test positive, experiences varied. Many did not receive the results of their tests at the time promised and were given no intervening explanation. The wait was agonising. Another complaint was that when promised repeat testing, within a certain period, this often did not happen. No explanation was given for the long delay.

One of the most controversial aspects of testing happened during Joan Power's period of research — between 1991 and 1994. Dr Power made a conscious decision not to tell the donors in her study that they were being tested, or, more importantly, that they had tested positively. At the Tribunal of Inquiry a number of the doctors giving evidence felt strongly that such a position was absolutely wrong.

> There was an ethical obligation to inform a person who had
> tested positive in any fashion, lest they wish to make the choice
> of having further investigation (*Tribunal of Inquiry Report*, p. 76).

In the Dáil, Máire Geoghegan-Quinn went further, lambasting the BTSB for using people as 'human guinea pigs'.

Unknown to himself, Donor L was part of Dr Power's

study for a two-year period. He tested positive on each of six occasions before being told in November 1993 that he had hepatitis C. Giving evidence at the Tribunal of Inquiry, he said that he was appalled and extremely angry at not being told that he was infected or being given the opportunity to have treatment.

Another donor, Kathleen, who has severe liver damage, was devastated to discover that her blood was being tested without her knowledge or consent, and that it was not, as she had been led to believe, being used for donations. She was doubly angry, she says, when she came across a letter sent from the Blood Bank in Cork in 1990. It said that she was 'a very important person, a VIP' and that many lives had been saved by the use of her blood.

So why did Dr Power not inform donors that they were being tested and that some of them were showing positive results? Her response to me was:

> There was not enough information available at the time to inform people who were showing positive on earlier, less reliable, tests.
>
> Certainly if we had known back in 1991 when testing was introduced that we couldn't have good answers, if we had known that it was going to take a long time to get to a situation where reliable testing was available, then I would have written to people. The difficulty of writing to people is that you must be prepared to follow it up. . . .
>
> I would not have had the resources to call in nearly two hundred people and say, 'I think you may have something wrong with your blood. It may be false positive, it may be true positive.' There is only one of me, although another consultant has been promised for years (Interview with the author, 21 May 1997).

In our interview, and from the Tribunal Report (p. 75), I formed the impression that Joan Power does not believe in giving information when, in her opinion, it is going to do more harm than good.

Up to fairly recently in Ireland people were not told about their positive tests necessarily. I think our public and legal systems have now moved on. Medical paternalism would have been a very credible view of how we interacted with people in the past (Interview with the author, 21 May 1997).

Despite Dr Power's view on the matter, it seems unthinkable that donors would not be informed when problems arose. In effect, people were denied crucial information about their own health, and so equally denied the option of seeking treatment. The Tribunal of Inquiry heard that within the BTSB itself there appeared to have been no agreed procedure, or even any discussion on the rights and wrongs of not telling donors if questions occurred. Dr Walsh apparently did inform people of the consequences of positive tests.

Given the level of shock and trauma that the crisis had caused, the immediate availability of appropriate counselling would seem to be a basic, urgent provision. However, what people needed and what they were offered were two different things.

Positive Action asked why women who were highly traumatised and often very angry could not avail of independent counsellors. Why were members of the very organisation that had caused the awful catastrophe present at counselling sessions? Was it, as some suspected, because the BTSB wanted to keep the lid on things, and to contain the problem?

Joan Power and the BTSB insisted that only a psychiatric/medical model of counselling would do:

At the first level, medical counselling was appropriate. I wouldn't do that differently; that's part of my training. The people who gave them information were people who had experience in sharing unwelcome and unwanted news. Part of medical counselling centres around what you are going to do. We would have invited them to bring someone with them, and then talked in privacy with refreshments and a nurse present.

The problem for Positive Action and others who were infected was that for a long time the BTSB didn't offer anything else. Many women said that they didn't want tea and sympathy. Medical information was one thing; but they were looking for support, for somewhere to express their strong feelings. The fact that the group sessions organised by the BTSB had BTSB staff present, served only to increase the fears of many women. Many of those present at such sessions in Dublin did not find it helpful either to be told to 'park [their] anger outside the door'.

While counselling was arranged by Dr Power for women at the Dublin Well Woman Centre, it amounted to only four sessions per person, and could not be availed of by the vast majority of women and men throughout the country.

Surely women could have chosen their own independent counsellors — as many eventually did. These counsellors were not necessarily from a medical background. In the aftermath of tragedies such as the Dunblane massacre, for instance, counsellors were immediately on the scene to help. Traumatised parents and children weren't asked to wait for the firearms experts. By contrast, women with hepatitis C were offered only a psychiatric/medical model of help, when what they urgently needed was a counsellor who was skilled in dealing with feelings.

In a heated exchange with Minister Brendan Howlin on the *Pat Kenny Show* in March 1997, Niamh Cosgrave, who has hepatitis C, forcibly expressed her views on what had happened on counselling:

> Bull. All you needed was a counsellor who knew how to deal with the trauma of life-threatening situations. It could have been a car crash, whatever.

Joan Power has taken a great deal of flak regarding the management of the situation, but she, in turn, has been critical of her own organisation, the BTSB.

At one stage in the Tribunal of Inquiry, she spoke of the 'burdensome bureaucratic layer' that was the hepatitis C co-ordinating committee of the BTSB. She went on to state that she felt that administrative support from the committee was 'not as it should be'. 'Archaic and bureaucratic' communications 'slowed things down', she told Judge Finlay.

It seemed that Dr Power was forced to juggle many different roles during the crisis: medical scientist, co-ordinator of screening, media person, and organiser of a national counselling programme. The consultant she had been promised when she first joined the BTSB never materialised :

> It was a highly pressurised time. I spent my days in Dublin and came back to Cork most nights to work till two a.m. in the morning. The same level of work went on for most of three years. I feel I've aged about ten years.

In addition, she had to cope with the trauma her own staff were experiencing:

> My own staff at the BTSB in Cork were devastated when all this happened. Many of them were young women under twenty-five who had gone there to work in a 'goodwill' service. They found the hostility that came from the public very hard to take.

There was also the chilling fact that vital information dating back to 1977 and to 1991 had never been disclosed to her by colleagues in Dublin. During her research, she was, she explains, 'totally unaware' of the 1991 memo from the Middlesex Hospital, which had informed the BTSB of a definite link between hepatitis C and Anti-D.

> Knowledge of this would have made a total difference. It would have meant that the product would have been changed before then.

There was criticism too for the Department of Health, which, she said, 'stalled' her attempts to locate all those women affected by hepatitis C and to publicise the fact that the virus was a problem for women other than those who had received Anti-D in 1977. The Department had refused to circulate a letter from her to GPs alerting them to the dangers.

Administration and communication within the BTSB would seem to have been chaotic even after the public were alerted to the crisis.

In March 1995, for instance, a year after the news of the problem broke, an independent inspection of Pelican House revealed an organisation still in chaos. Even basic hygiene standards were not present. Dirty blood bags were found in a filthy outhouse; there was no security in laboratory or storage areas or record of regular maintenance of the machine used to check blood for viruses. Not only that, the inspection found loose pieces of paper, hand altered with correcting fluid.

The adequacy of BTSB records is worrying, to say the least. In early 1997, the Blood Bank requested a donation of blood from a woman already infected with hepatitis C. And similarly, in early 1997, it emerged that a woman infected in the 1970s discovered that she had hepatitis C only when she went for testing. It appears that the BTSB had on file the fact that she had received blood from a suspect batch, but had failed to trace her. As Positive Action has said, with no national study, the true number of those infected remains unclear.

Furthermore, late in 1996, it had emerged that whilst the Blood Bank was aware that a Kilkenny nurse was infected with the HIV virus from a contaminated transfusion in 1985, it had failed to inform her. Attempting to trace batches of HIV-infected blood products, the BTSB wrote to hospitals, but omitted to say that the problem related to HIV.

When a crisis of such major proportion first emerged in 1994, it seems amazing that those charged with handling it should have been the BTSB. Despite being the organisation with the most knowledge concerning blood supplies, the plain fact remained — it was the Blood Bank that had caused the problem in the first place. At the very least, it must be argued, a committee of independent experts should have been immediately appointed by government to oversee the handling of the affair and to monitor strictly what the BTSB was doing.

Following the Tribunal of Inquiry, reforms of the Blood Bank were initiated. These reforms included the replacement of senior staff and the recruitment of more consultants. New screening systems have now been introduced and information technology will allow more efficient tracking of blood products. In addition, the old premises at Pelican House will be moved to St James's Hospital, Dublin, and in Cork refurbishment of premises is proposed.

However, whether we can safely trust the Blood Bank is an open question. PRO for the Association of GPs, Dr Mary Grehan believes that

> since the Blood Bank has made so many mistakes, it should be totally disbanded and rebuilt from scratch. Quite honestly, I also believe that all of the mistakes haven't yet come to light.

The BTSB itself now says that it is safer than at any other time, and is heading towards becoming a state-of-the-art organisation. That may be so, but keeping abreast of new developments will require government money on a regular basis. Will such vital investment in our safety be forthcoming? There is also the crucial necessity for constant monitoring to take place.

Either way, the sad fact remains that public confidence in the BTSB has been badly shattered. Judging from the recent, frequent, appeals for blood, it would seem that to regain the trust of ordinary people will take more than new computer programmes, new buildings, or the Quality Assurance Certificate that now hangs in BTSB offices.

Chapter Nine
Bloody Women

Everyone knew, and no one was telling. This was the feeling that many women had from the very start about the BTSB. At a time when they most needed to be treated with understanding, sensitivity and, above all, honesty, they met with evasions, half-truths and cover-ups. They were fobbed off, told not to worry, and kept in the dark about what was happening to their own bodies. Their agony and sense of isolation were compounded by the fact that they were kept apart.

'Anti-D women queue here' was the sign that greeted the hundreds of anxious women who found themselves in Pelican House on a cold, snowy February morning in 1994. They had come for screening in response to the public announcement linking hepatitis C with Anti-D. Worried, confused and fearful, they waited to meet the doctors — the men and women in white coats who would be able to tell them what it was all about, to give honest answers to important questions, to reassure them that everything possible was being done . . . and to show that little bit of humanity that would help to quell their mounting sense of panic.

What they encountered was a cold, clinical bureaucracy. There were forms to fill in, asking about ear piercing, tattoos, accidents with needles, drinking habits. In full hearing of others, including many anxious husbands, women were quizzed about previous sexual partners — questions that most found deeply offensive, questions that made them feel that they were to blame for what had happened.

In giving evidence to the Tribunal of Inquiry, many of the victims clearly believed that this apparently bizarre response by the Blood Transfusion Service Board was part of a determined attempt to divert responsibility and to mask the seriousness of what had occurred. The testimony of many of the victims suggests that it was a strategy of half-truths and cover-ups, which continued right up to 1997 when the Tribunal of Inquiry finally unearthed the truth.

Dorothy, who received contaminated Anti-D after the birth of her first child in 1977, comments:

> I didn't trust them from that very first morning. They were constantly fobbing us off — not answering our questions. My biggest fear all the time was that I wasn't being told the truth. It was only because I made a nuisance of myself that I found out anything at all.

'Don't worry. Go home and forget about it,' was the advice given to most, particularly those who had antibodies. For others, whose blood had already been tested and had shown virus positive (unknown to them), there was the nightmare of being abruptly thrown into an unreal world, where words like 'liver damage', 'cirrhosis' and 'biopsy' were being used.

Carmel, who received Anti-D in 1977 following a miscarriage, describes how the news was broken to her:

> I met a young doctor in Pelican House. She told me, 'Your results show that you are positive.' She talked about liver damage and then proceeded to say that I might go on to get liver cancer. That was it. I can't describe how devastated I was. Then I was left to stew for about seven weeks without any word — nothing other than the bits of information I picked up from the radio. I waited every day for a letter to arrive. I couldn't eat, couldn't sleep. I cried all the time and I had violent headaches.

Mary, a mother of four children, has mild liver damage as

a result of receiving contaminated Anti-D. She decided to ring her GP first.

> I heard on the radio that I could get a blood test from my own doctor. That made me feel a little better, but when I rang him, he said that he had heard nothing, that he was waiting for information himself.

The weeks following the announcement in February 1994 were a chronicle of delays, confusion and uncertainty. Women found that they were being rushed through the testing process. But test results could take anything up to seven or eight weeks — an agonising wait. There were no explanations from the Blood Bank. Difficulties presented themselves at every corner: copies of test results were not supplied; information was minimised, played-down. 'Everyone knew, but no one was telling,' says Mary. The women felt that they were deliberately being kept in the dark, being fed only small drops of the truth. It was only when medical reports were prepared for the Tribunal of Inquiry that some women finally discovered the seriousness of what had happened to them.

Apart from the issue of testing, victims also complained of the ineptitude of the BTSB in offering only basic information about the implications of living with hepatitis C. One woman recalls being told not to share a toothbrush and to keep razors separately, but when she asked whether she should avoid becoming pregnant, no clear information was forthcoming. The same lack of information was apparent when women asked whether it was safe to drink alcohol or to use other medication. They were given no clear guidelines regarding sexual contact, although such questions were of immediate and critical importance to them and to their partners. There was no real explanation of the difference between 'mild', 'moderate' and 'severe'. Advice on the drug Interferon was limited. The side-effects of the drug were brushed aside as 'flu-like symptoms', but many women suffered much worse side-effects, including hair-loss, nausea and mouth ulcers. A considerable number of women in different parts of the country failed to receive *any* basic information about hepatitis C.

Over a year later, in 1995, many had still not received copies of their own test results, or detailed information on the type of hepatitis C virus they had. The deep frustration felt by women found a channel in Positive Action. The organisation invited an independent expert from England, Dr Geoffrey Duisheiko, to address some of their fears and to provide the information the women felt was so long overdue. A leading virologist, Dr Duisheiko had experience of hepatitis C. One woman who attended the meeting at which he spoke later commented:

> He at least treated us like rational, intelligent adults — people who had a perfect right to the truth.

Women whose tests had shown antibodies were left dangling. They were expected to come and go for blood tests at the Blood Bank and were told not to worry, that things would be all right. But they didn't feel all right. Many had been unwell for a long time. Early attempts to refer them to hepatology units in the hospitals were blocked by the BTSB.

In July 1994, Dr Whelton of the Cork Regional Hospital, Chairman of the Hepatology Group, wrote to the Department of Health, asking for all groups, including those with antibodies, to be referred by the Blood Bank. It was safer, Dr Whelton and his colleagues argued, and it would also help to ease worries. The letter read:

> The Group feels strongly that to exclude any of these groups would be incorrect and might be construed as negligence.

It was passed on to the BTSB who refused to accept the

advice, arguing that the women referred to were well, and were not patients.

Marian received infected Anti-D and has liver damage.

> We had to fight to see Dr Whelton at the Regional Hospital. I asked the Blood Bank on numerous occasions, but the answer was negative. 'No need,' they said. 'You're fine. Go home and forget about it.' But I had symptoms of hepatitis C for years. I had a permanent skin rash since 1977. The BTSB never asked me how I was feeling. In the end, out of pure frustration, I got a referral letter from my GP. I know lots of women who did that. And I also know women who believed the Blood Bank, who were going for testing once a year or so, only later — much later — to discover that they had liver damage.

The Tribunal of Inquiry was later to state that the BTSB was:

> . . . inadequate in its reaction in failing to agree in July 1994 to the proposals of a group of Hepatologists for the referral of persons proving positive on testing to Hepatological Units (*Tribunal of Inquiry Report*, p. 150).

Those who had tested virus positive were referred to hepatology units. The next step for them was a liver biopsy. Between March and the end of May 1994, about 460 women went for liver biopsies. It's an unpleasant, difficult and dangerous procedure. While the patient is fully conscious and lying on her side, a long needle is inserted into the liver area. She must breath deeply while this is happening to lift the rib cage. If a patient is nervous, it is more painful.

Those women who have had biopsies emphasise the need for special sensitivity and kindness. But in many cases women received no advance information from BTSB staff of what to expect. Hospital treatment varied. In some parts of the country the procedure was handled with care and thoughtfulness. In others, especially in Dublin, the experience was described as a nightmare. Overcrowding and lack of proper facilities or adequate aftercare added to the trauma that the women were already experiencing.

In a submission to Minister Brendan Howlin in June 1994 Positive Action described some of these experiences:

> One woman in St James' Hospital Dublin had her biopsy carried out in a public ward, without the curtain being pulled and without a nurse present to hold her hand. She felt like a criminal.
>
> Another woman in the same hospital, recovering from a biopsy in a four-bedded ward, woke from a sleep to find two men occupying two of the beds.
>
> One woman hadn't a scan taken prior to or during her biopsy. When she returned on the appointed day three weeks later she was told a piece of her kidney, not her liver, was taken and she would need a further biopsy. There was no contact made with her in the intervening period to explain an error had occurred.
>
> One woman from Co. Donegal was discharged early in the morning following her biopsy. She wasn't aware that this would happen and hadn't a lift arranged for the long journey home until that afternoon.
>
> One woman was placed in a HIV ward following her biopsy in St James' Hospital. On objecting strongly, she had to wait some time before an alternative bed could be found.

Such experiences are not, alas, exclusive to women with hepatitis C. They are relatively common to other patients. However, because of the treatment that the hepatitis C women had already received from the BTSB such hospital experiences served to compound their feelings of isolation and loneliness.

As part of the biopsy procedures women had to give blood samples in hospitals. They were confused and angered to find red stickers attached to their charts and samples. There was no explanation, and it added to their feeling of being tainted and stigmatised.

There were other areas too in which they felt stigmatised. In some cases, dentists declined to give treatment to women who they discovered had hepatitis C. Women awaiting surgery found that they had been rescheduled to the end of the theatre list because they were told that the theatre would have to be sterilised.

Women felt that information about hepatitis C should have been circulated by the BTSB to inform both the medical profession and the general public, to counteract the hurtful effects of misinformation.

Maura contracted hepatitis C through an infected blood transfusion. She describes a recent experience (in 1997), which she says left her 'feeling like a leper'. It happened when she went for a routine x-ray to a dental hospital in Dublin:

> The radiologist had me all set up for x-ray, then she opened my chart. When she saw hepatitis C all hell broke lose. She took my gown off and said HIV and hepatitis C patients needed a special gown. Then she proceeded to put cling film on the door handles, all over the machines, even covering the scope on the ceiling. She put two pairs of gloves on and even covered the bite that went into my mouth with cling-film. I didn't wait to see the specialist. I just ran. I ran into Stephen's Green and sobbed my heart out. Before that, I'd had no hang up about hepatitis C. I was quite open about it. But for weeks afterwards I was tense and nervous. It even affected the sexual relationship between my partner and myself.

Most damaging of all was that, when the news first broke, women were kept apart. At a time when they most needed the emotional support of others who were in the same situation, many of the women felt that the BTSB deliberately impeded that contact.

Marian remembers how she felt:

> Every time I went for a blood test, I'd look around at other women, thinking, 'Is she in the same boat as me?' I was going for weekly tests. The first thing I'd ask was, 'Is there anyone else like me? Could I meet them? Do other people ask?' The BTSB told me that they couldn't give information. But I left my name and phone number just the same.

On 6 April 1994, Jane O'Brien met with Dr Emer Lawlor of the BTSB and asked whether it would be possible for her to supply a letter, which would then be circulated to other women who had undergone screening. Several other women who were infected shared Jane's concern and said that their phone numbers could be used in a contact letter. However, three days after a letter had been sent to the BTSB, Consultant Haematologist Dr Emer Lawlor was in contact to say that there could be logistical problems in distributing such a letter.

Despite lobbying from the Council for the Status of Women, nothing was done. Eventually a letter arrived from the BTSB, explaining their concern for patient confidentiality and telling the women that it could not distribute the proposed letter. It ended:

> To issue such a letter would be to endorse formally your group ahead of others. It might also alarm some women to receive a letter from your group that had been distributed by the Board.

However, the BTSB also failed to provide any other form of much-needed contact. And besides, women were already alarmed. They were alarmed and frightened because they were alone. What they desperately needed was contact with others. In the end, they were left to struggle as best they could to find each other.

Besides needing to contact each other, professional counselling was urgently called for. Overnight the lives of women and their families had been turned upside down. How could they come to terms with such a shattering blow? How would they face an uncertain future which would undoubtedly hold more suffering, and perhaps even an early death?

The reaction by the BTSB was to set up its own 'counselling' for those screening positive. The counselling was held with members of the BTSB present — the very

people who were responsible for creating the appalling
tragedy. According to Dorothy from Cork:

> They weren't counselling meetings at all. Dr Joan Power of
> the BTSB was there; she chaired the meetings. Then there
> were nurses from the BTSB present and a clinical psycholo-
> gist, Eddie Hogan, whom they had appointed. How could
> you possibly feel free to show your feelings, or talk about
> your fears? They were trying to manage us. They thought
> that they had a group of ignorant little women who could be
> fooled. But we saw through it. We weren't ignorant at all.

Dorothy asked about having counselling sessions without
the BTSB presence. Her suggestion was rejected.

> We were told that medical questions might arise which Mr
> Hogan couldn't deal with.

The women reacted to the BTSB with intensified feelings
of distrust and anger. Many felt that the real purpose
behind the actions of the BTSB was one of control — to
keep the lid on things.

In Dublin, women were told to 'park their anger at the
door'. Instead of counselling sessions, the women were
being given lecture-information talks. The paternalistic
response of the medical profession in this situation fell far
short of what was required. Instead of openness, communication and equal participation, which the women so
badly sought, the BTSB remained hide-bound by the
conventional doctor-knows-best approach, and by the
politics of containment and damage limitation.

The frightening reality for the women had dawned: they
couldn't trust the BTSB or the state to protect their interests. For the truth to emerge, they would have to fight their
own battle.

It is not surprising that at this point a strong independent lobby group began to emerge. It was a group
that finally became a force to be reckoned with — a
power to remove the lid and allow the truth to emerge.

Chapter Ten

United We Stand

'A bunch of hysterical women' — that was how one government official described Positive Action. The women had come together out of a sense of desperation and fear. With virtually no previous political experience and only hepatitis C in common, it seemed that this small group of mostly middle-aged, full-time mothers, would be easily dismissed by the powerful institutions of the state and the forcefulness of politicians.

After the first days of shock newspaper headlines, hepatitis C virtually disappeared from the public gaze. The impression was that the problem was now under control; lives were safe in the competent hands of caring professionals. Yet the experience of those diagnosed as having hepatitis C was quite different. Far from being comforted, they felt abandoned, dismissed and patronised.

Jane O'Brien, chairperson of Positive Action, and the driving force behind it recalls:

> 'Don't worry. It's all right; all is being taken care of by the BTSB,' was what we were told. But for me and other women such statements simply didn't ring true. I wanted to know if other people were being treated in the same evasive fashion as I was and I wanted to make sure that we would be told the truth.
>
> We wanted to know why this had happened in the first place. And why were we only told about it seventeen years later? But there was no response. Our feeling was that the

BTSB was involved in a damage limitation exercise. That's why we were keen to raise our concerns independently.

Quite by chance, Jane O'Brien had been in contact with two other women who had hepatitis C. One, from Dublin, had received Anti-D in 1977, and had just begun treatment with Interferon, a cancer drug. Her condition was serious. The other woman was living in the south west and had received contaminated Anti-D in 1993. Jane O'Brien herself received Anti-D in 1985 and 1991, following the birth of her two daughters.

> When I spoke to these women, the alarm bells began to ring. We had a whole spectrum of contamination which went right past the time when they introduced their own hepatitis screening, and past 1977 which was the year constantly spoken of by the BTSB. Now I realised how horrendous the problem really was. It made me more determined than ever to find out the truth.

In April 1994, Jane O'Brien asked the BTSB to circulate a letter to other hepatitis C victims. It read:

> Dear friend,
>
> We are writing to you as fellow hepatitis C/Anti-D sufferers. We know the personal suffering, fear and isolation you may be going through. This letter which is kindly being distributed by the Blood Transfusion Service Board is to judge interest in establishing a support group for Anti-D women. Such a group would enable women to form contacts with others in the same situation living in their area. It would help greatly if you would complete the following questionnaire to enable us to build up a wider picture of the situation.

The letter was signed by Jane O'Brien and several other hepatitis C sufferers. They didn't foresee a problem. At a previous meeting with Dr Emer Lawlor of the BTSB, she had indicated that such a letter would be acceptable. However, the formal response was different. Replying later to Ms O'Brien's letter, Dr Lawlor's view seemed to

have changed. She spoke of 'complex issues', which
needed 'careful consideration'. On 3 May 1994 the Board
of the BTSB stated:

> The Board cannot and will not provide any group with de-
> tails of individual cases.

It would not be possible to distribute a letter. However,
no alternative means of communication for women was
offered either. A door was firmly shut.

The women were angry, but undeterred. A different
strategy was called for. Contact had been made with
Anne Taylor, then chairperson of the Council for the
Status of Women. With her help, they got in touch with a
number of politicians in an effort to have questions asked
in the Dáil.

At home, Jane O'Brien's telephone began to ring.
Women were beginning to find each other. The calls
increased in number.

> If I had a cup of tea, I left the phone off the hook. I had a
> constant stream of calls, many from women who said that
> they wanted to become more involved.

That contact led to a small meeting in early May 1994.
There was a unanimous feeling that a group had to be
formed — an independent group that would be a voice
for women.

A ripple effect started. In Cork two women put an ad-
vertisement in the local paper, giving contact numbers.
Others were featured on local radio and in the news-
papers, telling their stories. All over the country more and
more women were exchanging telephone numbers, talking to each other. When three women told their
individual stories on Gay Byrne's morning radio programme, there was a flood of new inquiries.

In June 1994, the first meeting of Positive Action was
held at Wynn's Hotel. It was an unforgettable occasion,

one that was charged with emotion. About seventy people were expected. An incredible three hundred women, from as far away as Donegal and Kerry, showed up. Most had to remain standing.

Carmel, an early member of Positive Action, remembers that meeting:

> I can still feel the terror that night in Wynn's Hotel. We were all so frightened. We had no idea what we were facing into — whether it was good, bad or indifferent Amazingly, we had been told by the Blood Bank that it wouldn't change our lives in any way, but that was so untrue. This bombshell had been dropped in our laps and they seemed to expect us to act as if nothing was happening .

Valerie, who has severe liver damage, recalls turning up at Wynn's that evening:

> The organisers carefully divided us into small groups, making sure that we could share with women whose hepatitis C was at a similar stage of development to ours. I was on Interferon and very frightened. I can't tell you how reassuring it was to meet others in the same position as myself.

Joan Power, regional director of the BTSB, was asked to attend the meeting to give information. She was inundated with questions. Jane O'Brien says:

> My memory is of just one microphone and this huge queue of people wanting to ask questions, desperate for information.

Following the meeting, Jane O'Brien spent the weekend writing a detailed submission to Minister Brendan Howlin, chronicling what had been talked about at the meeting and the concerns women had expressed over the telephone. Representatives from Positive Action were invited to his office to talk. They were hopeful: the door of officialdom seemed to be creaking open.

But the experience was to prove disappointing. The group had expected up-front answers, but instead they came away feeling disillusioned, with their questions side-stepped. Jane O'Brien realised that they would have to battle every inch of the way to get the healthcare they needed, and the urgent answers to which they felt entitled.

> It wasn't a matter of not trusting the Department. There was no antagonism in the early stages. It was rather a case of their agenda being different to ours. Officialdom, it seemed, was intent on getting on with the business of running the country. We were saying, 'Hey, wait a minute, listen to us. You can't just ignore this dreadful thing.'

Regular submissions to the Department were made by Positive Action, yet there was no feedback and no information. It appeared to be a one-way discussion. All that was forthcoming was the possibility of an *Expert Group Report* and bland assurances that the women's health would be taken care of. For the women in Positive Action it became painfully clear that if anything were to happen they would have to do it themselves.

Minister Howlin finally set up an Expert Group to inquire into the issue. Positive Action made submissions asking numerous questions relating to lack of adequate counselling, information and healthcare. Among a whole series of detailed medical questions put to the Expert Group, one vital section asked about BTSB screening of donors:

> Positive Action is aware of women who received contaminated Anti-D in 1991 and 1993. Was infected Anti-D manufactured prior to 1991, left in circulation? Why wasn't Anti-D which was manufactured prior to the hepatitis C screening scrapped completely in 1991 and a safe imported product introduced?

Such crucial questions were not answered until the Tribunal of Inquiry finally began its hearings in November 1996.

In an effort to get answers to some of the medical questions the group personally invited Dr Geoffrey Duisheiko

over from London to address a meeting in Liberty Hall.
He spoke to a packed audience of over five hundred
women.

Mary, a mother of four children, is an executive member of Positive Action.

> I remember travelling up from Cork for that meeting.
> Another woman came with me. We couldn't get
> accommodation anywhere — only a double bed. So we took
> that .

The frank and honest approach of Dr Duisheiko came like
a breath of fresh air. But he also confirmed their worst
fears — that the seriousness of their situation was being
hidden from them.

Campaigning was stepped up. Positive Action realised
that the key to getting results lay with the politicians. Jane
O'Brien explains:

> We became very conscious that the Minister for Health and
> the Taoiseach had the control and power that could be of vi-
> tal importance to us. We also lobbied the opposition, letting
> the political establishment know what our issues were, giv-
> ing them the ammunition to instigate debates on hepatitis C
> — an issue which the government clearly didn't want to
> confront. When there were Dáil debates we made sure that
> the public gallery was packed with women from Positive
> Action.

By now the demands of Positive Action were clear:

- Free, quality healthcare

- Proper up-to-date information

- Counselling independent of the BTSB

- Copies of test results.

The issue of compensation depended on the outcome of
the *Expert Group Report*.

Towards the end of 1994, the Fianna Fáil/Labour

coalition fell. Michael Noonan became the new Minister for Health. Positive Action waited to see whether he would take action on these vital issues, whether he would have the courage to address the question of who was responsible, and why.

Despite the constraints that the Expert Group was working under, its final report, released in April 1995, astounded the women. Prior to its publication, the BTSB had been saying that the contamination was an Act of God. When the report was published, the women discovered that their infection wasn't just a mistake — that the whole trauma could have been prevented. Now it became clear that basic procedural rules had been broken. Jane O'Brien recalls the reaction:

> Women were shocked and angry. They were shocked to find out that they shouldn't have been sick and that this whole tragedy could have been prevented if simple cautionary steps according to the BTSB's own guidelines had been taken.

Outrage among the members of Positive Action mounted, but they quickly learned the value of channelling their feelings into political action — becoming negotiators rather than just angry women.

Taking on the mammoth weight of state institutions was a daunting prospect. For the first year, Positive Action had no office. Executive members — ordinary women, most with families to care for — were dealing with subscriptions, correspondence, medical research and legal matters, from their kitchen tables. And they were paying their own expenses.

In early 1995, Positive Action began taking legal advice. Jane O'Brien says that it was to prove invaluable.

> There was huge trust in our legal advisors headed by John Rogers — huge personal warmth of affection. This, together with the loyalty and trust of our members, combined to make us a very strong team.

The power of the media was also harnessed: RTÉ's *Prime Time*, the *Pat Kenny Show*, and the national press began asking questions. Women who had never spoken out before took their courage in both hands and told their stories in public. It was a learning experience for everyone, and it helped to increase confidence and to fuel the women's determination to secure justice.

Behind the scenes, strong campaigning continued. All over the country, women were writing to TDs, calling into constituency clinics helping to keep the issue alive. A constant flow of information was sent to politicians. Positive Action pulled out the stops and used the political establishment in every way they could, letting politicians know the enormity of what was wrong and what needed to be done about it.

In September 1995, the issue of compensation was put out front by Michael Noonan, Minister for Health. There was also a commitment to healthcare. A tribunal would pay compensation, but only on an *ex-gratia* basis — there would be no legal admission of liability or apology by the state. Claimants were given only a month to accept an award if it was granted. And an acceptance would mean full and final settlement — all rights to go to court would be waived. One senior official in the Department of Health described the proposed compensation tribunal as 'a benevolent institution, not a court'.

Positive Action members reacted angrily to the announcement of the compensation tribunal, which had been made while they were still in negotiation with the Department of Health. They voted to reject the tribunal, arguing that its powers were too limited. What they wanted was a system that would admit liability, and a statutory framework that would cover healthcare and compensation matters. At a meeting of the Oireachtas Social Affairs committee in October 1995, Positive Action outlined its objections and told of 'mischievous and threatening' letters that had been received from the Chief State Solicitor. The letters informed women that if they chose to reject the tribunal and go to court, the resulting litigation would be 'fully defended by the State'.

Michael Noonan dug his heels in, determined to push the women along the compensation route. He told them bluntly that there would be no more concessions. If they didn't accept what was being offered, the door would be firmly shut.

Relations sank to an all-time low. Jane O'Brien explains:

> We felt that it was very unjust. It was one of the lowest points for Positive Action. If simple changes had been made, the issues could have been resolved.

To be treated in such a dismissive way was crushing for women who had given such huge commitment and time to arguing their case. Now they were facing the full brunt of the system. At this point, it would have been very easy to give up — many were making enormous personal sacrifices by holding out. But Minister Noonan had not realised that the struggle of these women was never about money — it was about justice. They held out. According to Jane O'Brien:

> We knew that this was so wrong and we kept going. At various stages, the Minister could have made changes that would have closed the book, but the Minister didn't and so we continued our campaign.

Tension increased. Michael Noonan's Compensation Tribunal was under daily attack, as was his determination to push women to accept. Positive Action was mindful that the High Court might have to be the ultimate arbitrator. Members were also conscious that the case of one of their fellow sufferers — Brigid McCole — was in its preliminary stages, and would, they hoped, be heard early in 1996. Jane O'Brien says:

> The Minister had shut the door, but we felt that the back-burner was still bubbling over.

The major turning point for Positive Action was ringed with sadness. On 2 October 1996, Brigid McCole died. She never got to the High Court, but her death had finally awoken the public conscience to the gravity of the situation and the full horror of what had been going on behind closed doors. Jane O'Brien recalls:

> There was a huge awareness that this was a scandal. Up to then we had always felt that in the eyes of the Department of Health and various ministers we were regarded as a nuisance — people to be barely tolerated because we were victims. But the issue changed: here was a scandal which, it was said, was worse than anything the Beef Tribunal had thrown up.

Opposition pressure for a Tribunal of Inquiry mounted. A motion from the Progressive Democrats condemned the Minister for failing to accept political responsibility for the hepatitis C crisis.

Fianna Fáil's Máire Geoghegan-Quinn demanded that the scheme for compensation be stood down while a judicial inquiry proceeded. In view of Mrs McCole's death no other victim should be:

> dragged through the courts by the state and no other person should have to go through such trauma and pressure to find out why they were infected (Dáil, 8 October 1996).

In the end a Tribunal of Inquiry became inevitable but whilst the terms of reference of the Tribunal were widely accepted, there was one remark made by the Minister that proved too much for Positive Action. In a damning Dáil speech, Mr Noonan criticised Brigid McCole's right to have her case heard in court:

> Could her solicitors not, in seeking a test case for the hundreds of hepatitis C cases on their books, have selected a

plaintiff in a better condition to sustain the stress of a High Court case? Was it in the interest of their client to attempt to run her case, not only in the High Court but also in the media and in the Dáil simultaneously? (Dáil, 16 October 1996)

Joan O'Brien clearly recalls:

> That was it. We couldn't sit and listen to Brigid's memory being insulted.

Seven members of Positive Action's executive left the public gallery. 'The Minister will have to apologise, or resign,' they told the reporters waiting outside the Dáil.

The Minister apologised.

A Tribunal of Inquiry was set to go ahead. After two-and-a-half years of being patronised and dismissed, Positive Action members were finally to learn the chilling truth about what had happened to them.

The healthcare package for which they had fought had finally been put into law in Spring 1996. In October 1997, a Bill was adopted, making compensation statutory — another of the goals for which they had been fighting.

The small group of confused and shocked women who began Positive Action had come a long way. Far from being hysterical, these ordinary women had found a voice and a new political consciousness. They had emerged as a powerful campaigning body which successfully challenged the state. And, with over seven hundred members, they had truly become a force to be reckoned with.

Reflecting now on the campaign, Jane O'Brien says:

> What Minister Noonan and the other politicians failed to realise was the depth of feeling that the women had. They thought it was a problem which would go away if they simply paid money. We in turn were quick to realise that because the odds were stacked against us, we had to channel our feelings of anger and frustration. To be heard we had to be credible, to adopt a professional approach which would convince, persuade and would lead people to understand

where we were coming from. I think that we were very measured and controlled because that's the way the system works. It would have been so easy to brand us as hysterical women, but we were never going to give them that excuse.

Most recently, Positive Action has been actively pursuing the issue of a criminal investigation by the state. It has supplied new evidence to the Garda Commissioner, together with letters of complaint.

It also continues to act as watchdog to ensure the full delivery of proper healthcare and compensation. Up-to-date information has to be researched. Then there is the most basic need of all — to be there as a support for women whose future is bleak and uncertain. Some, like Mrs McCole, will die early. Jane O'Brien says:

> We always knew that there was a longer-term agenda. One chapter is closed, but as we remind ourselves, it's a big book.

The story of Positive Action reflects bleakly on modern Ireland. It is an Ireland where the knee-jerk reaction of our elected representatives and those in charge of state bodies is to sweep everything under the carpet. It is an Ireland where individuals must guard against the negligence — and sometimes injustice — of the state itself.

In order to protect ourselves, must we become watchdogs engaged in struggle, as the Positive Action members were forced to do? Must we as citizens now take responsibility for ensuring that our institutions become more open and are held accountable for their actions?

Chapter Eleven

Wrongful Acts and Failures:

Tribunal of Inquiry

On 5 November 1996 the Tribunal of Inquiry finally began. At last the story would be told. It was an inquiry long awaited, long overdue, but one that Minister Noonan had vehemently resisted, arguing that his major concern was with maintaining the blood supply, and not damaging public confidence. In the end, he was forced into agreeing to a judicial inquiry. However, this was to be a Tribunal different from others. It wasn't about power or money, or about corruption in high places. It was a Tribunal about ordinary men and women who had become caught up in an extraordinary twentieth-century nightmare. It was about pain and suffering brought about by the negligence of a state agency.

'An appalling but straightforward simple story,' was how James Nugent SC, Tribunal Counsel, described it in his opening statement. As it transpired, the story wasn't quite so simple. A wealth of shocking new evidence was about to be revealed — evidence concerning 'missing files' in the BTSB, lack of proper licensing by the National Drugs Advisory Board, warnings from GPs which were ignored. None of this evidence had come to light in the 1995 *Report of the Expert Group*.

On the opening pages of the 197-page published report, Judge Thomas Finlay describes his experience of listening to the individual testimonies of victims as 'a deeply distressing and very emotive experience'. He goes on to say:

> Our task, however, has been to ascertain the facts which have been referred to us and reach the conclusions requested in an entirely detached and unemotive manner leaving aside great sympathy for the victims.

Justice Finlay meant business. There was to be no legal manoeuvring, no unnecessary wrangles, no time-wasting. Throughout the six weeks of the Tribunal, he could be heard clarifying points, translating legalistic jargon into understandable language, chastising the lawyers for needless repetition or for straying from the point.

With fifty years of experience behind him, his had been a varied and colourful career. He was the judge who oversaw the inquiry into the 1995 Lansdowne Road soccer match; the lawyer who successfully defended Captain James Kelly in the 1970 arms trial; and the man who presented the Irish case when the state took the UK government before the European Court of Human Rights. More recently, he was the judge who presided over the Supreme Court in the controversial X case, when the Supreme Court overturned the High Court injunction preventing the young girl concerned from travelling to the UK for an abortion.

Outside the tribunal building, in leafy Adelaide Road, people bustled about their daily business. On the steps, cameramen waited, eager to catch the comings and goings of the central players in this grotesque human tragedy.

Inside the bland airless tribunal room, the din of the city could be heard. The lawyers clustered around the long wooden tables, heads together, passing notes to and fro. At the back of the room, straining to hear, sat some of those infected with hepatitis C. It wasn't easy to listen to testimonies from those whose negligence had shattered their lives. But it was something that they wanted to do — a necessary process to be undertaken so that they could close yet another chapter in this long, harrowing saga.

Carmel is a grandmother in her sixties. She has hepatitis C and liver damage. She explained why she attended the Tribunal:

> I came to the Inquiry because I wanted to put faces on the faceless. I wanted to hear the awful truth from the lips of those responsible. It was a painful experience, but it has helped me to get over my anger. I never thought that the truth would come out.

Marian, sick with hepatitis C for seventeen years, also attended:

> Although I found it very upsetting, it really was the best thing that I have done. Despite the coldness and indifference that I felt was coming from many of the officials, I genuinely got a sense that justice would at last be heard. It also allowed a healing process to begin, for some of my anger to drain away.

Maura, who contracted hepatitis C through a transfusion of contaminated blood, felt intense anger as she sat listening to members of the Blood Bank giving evidence:

> Some of them seemed so complacent, so arrogant. At the same time, I'm glad I went. It was like putting a name on what had happened, taking us all out of the limbo we had been living in.

Mary, a member of Positive Action, was a regular attendee at the Tribunal. The long train journey she had to take to get to Dublin left her drained, but she was determined to see the truth come out.

> I found the Tribunal brilliant. There was nothing let slip. It was marvellous to see the job so well done.

Not everyone could face the experience though. Maeve, a fifty-year-old mother from Co. Offaly, made a special effort to travel up to Dublin. At the last minute, she felt that she just couldn't go in.

> I got right up the steps of the Tribunal building, right to the glass doors, but in the end I was too frightened. I thought that I might hear something which would upset me even more.

* * *

Each day, proceedings began at 10.30 in the morning. The lawyers arrived, carrying their boxes filled with the mountains of evidence to be presented; the stenographers sat poised ready to process about 190 pages of testimony each day. Microphones were tested, overheads switched on. Then there was a hush as Judge Finlay took his seat.

It was to be a tribunal full of contrasts: on the one hand, the clinical, detached evidence of the scientists and medical experts, the bureaucratic preciseness of the departmental officials; on the other hand, the sad, human stories — testimonies of lives wrecked and hopes shattered.

There were occasional moments of black humour, such as when, for instance, James Nugent described the Department of Health's backdating of licences for Anti-D (which hid serious breaches of regulations) as something akin to 'The Starship Enterprise':

> In attempting to untangle the events which occurred, one was hampered by the fact that the ordinary concept, that the present follows the past and precedes the future, does not appear to have applied in this particular case.

There was the unexpected evidence of a clerical officer at the Tribunal of Inquiry who had overheard special advisor Dr Tim Collins making a call to Brendan Howlin on his mobile phone, to tell him that he had not been 'absolutely shafted' by a former secretary in the Department of Health.

As John Hegarty, Medical Director of the liver treatment unit in St Vincent's Hospital, gave his evidence, there was a chill in the room. He told the Tribunal that between 60 and 70 per cent of those with the virus will go on to develop various levels of liver disease, occasionally ending in death — as in the case of his patient, Brigid McCole.

Then there were the witnesses from the Blood Bank. Cecily Cunningham, chief biochemist, sat squeezing her husband's hand before she gave evidence, and when on the stand, constantly turned to look at him as she spoke.

'I just ploughed on,' she said, as she described using plasma from Patient Y in 1989, knowing it could be contaminated.

Her boss, Dr Walsh, broke the rules in 1976, when he allowed Anti-D to be made from the plasma of Patient X, a decision that resulted in death sentences for those affected. At the Tribunal he said:

> I've been very deeply upset by this. I regret I didn't ask more questions. I am wholly and totally devastated by my lack of response at the time.

Dr Jack O'Riordan, former National Director of the BTSB, eighty-three years old and shaky, resisted giving evidence and had eventually to be subpoenaed to attend the Tribunal. He said that he couldn't remember Patient X or much about the affair. 'Let us face reality, sir,' he said to Judge Finlay. 'I cannot recall a hell of a lot of these things. How could I?'

Those whose lives have been shattered by the actions of BTSB officials had no trouble remembering what had happened to them.

On a bleak Thursday afternoon in December they told

their own painful stories. Some, fighting back tears, told
of their fears for themselves and for their families. They
were not alone in their agony. Several times Judge Finlay
halted proceedings to allow those who were silently
listening to the testimony to wipe tears from their eyes
and to compose themselves. Here were stories that moved
even the most hardened of lawyers and journalists.

Forty-one-year-old Paula from Kilkenny has fibrosis of
the liver. She told of her medical prognosis: another ten
years of life if she is lucky.

> The realisation of having to face premature death through
> no fault of my own is a very difficult situation to come to
> terms with. For me, as Brigid McCole became iller it was like
> looking into a mirror down the road for me. I felt that when
> Brigid died, a piece of me died.

Gerry, a fifty-year-old schoolteacher, became infected
through a transfusion and has seen his life 'closing
down'. With tears in his eyes, he described his sense of
utter panic when he realised that his own children might
have been infected by him. He also described the private
hell in which many other men and women are trapped
because of the stigma associated with hepatitis C.

> There are cases of children being victimised, of people fear-
> ful of losing jobs.

He knew of one family who had told no one that their
dad had hepatitis C:

> . . . living with this little secret as if it was something shame-
> ful, that was their fault. I can see how it is actually affecting
> them, poisoning their family life.

As they listened to Bríd McCole describe the hell that her
mother was forced to go through, people wept openly.
Twice Bríd herself was unable to bear the strain, rushing
from the room, utterly distraught.

All my mother ever wanted was the truth. It was never about money.

On another day, Donor L, a family man in his fifties, spoke from behind a screen. He described his feelings of distress and fury when he discovered that the blood donations he had been conscientiously giving since 1991 had tested positive for hepatitis C and were being used as part of a research project by the BTSB. At no time, had he been informed that they were being used for the purpose of testing, and not until 1993 was he told that any form of positive result had arisen. He believed that he was still giving valuable donations of blood. He wondered whether he might have benefited from earlier treatment.

On the afternoon of Friday, 24 January 1997, Michael Noonan arrived to give evidence. There was an air of anticipation in the packed room. Here was the stuff of real courtroom drama — a government minister forced to account for himself. Hands folded neatly on the desk, lips pursed, the Minister looked cool and assured. Facing him was the tall, stooping figure of Senior Counsel John Rogers. Several months earlier Mr Noonan had criticised John Rogers, as the lawyer acting for Brigid McCole, for bringing a dying woman before the courts.

Central to the questioning of the Minister was the discovery of the 'missing file' in 1996. The file showed that the Blood Bank had known in 1976 that Patient X had 'infective hepatitis'. Leaning towards Minister Noonan, eyebrows raised, Mr Rogers sought to ascertain how this crucial piece of evidence had never been disclosed to the Dáil:

> I put it to you Minister that your failure is evidenced by the fact that you never, until this Tribunal was established, sought to ascertain what was the clear knowledge of the BTSB as regards infection of the woman in 1976, that it is only here that this has been publicly acknowledged.

It was only here that Minister Noonan lost his cool:

> I have dealt for two years with this major health crisis in the
> department, and in my view I have dealt with it with an awful
> lot of credit and the things I did right far outweighs anything I
> did wrong, and I resent, Mr Rogers, you talking about the
> failure of the Minister for Health in this respect.

Helen, a mother of two children, had travelled up from
Thurles to hear the Minister. She listened wearily to the
dog-fight that was taking place. She had wanted to know
what had been going on in official minds — how much
they had known, but not told.

> I sat quietly listening to Noonan fobbing off questions, get-
> ting himself off the hook. But inside I was seething. I wanted
> desperately to get him on his own, to pin him down and tell
> him just how much hepatitis C has ruined my life, how
> much my family has suffered.

When Judge Finlay's report was finally published in
March 1997, it made for grim reading. There was severe
criticism of individual officials of the BTSB, unprecedented
strong language about the 'wrongful acts', 'failures', and
'complete and inadequate and non-existent' response that
had led to the catastrophe.

The report found that the Board not only was unable to
face up to the consequences of those acts, but also refused
to face the consequences of what had been done in relation to Patient X.

> . . . the major responsibility in connection with the safety of
> the raw material consisting of the donations of blood rests
> with the medical staff of the Blood Transfusion Service . . .
> the contamination of the eventual blood product arose from
> a total failure to adhere to the standards of donor selection
> (*Tribunal of Inquiry Report*, p. 23).

It found that much of the crucial evidence regarding what
had happened had not been available to the Expert Group
set up to investigate the causes of the tragedy. If it had
been, the report said, it would have constituted conclusions

of 'improper acts' and 'wrongful practices'.

According to the report, Dr John (Jack) O'Riordan bore the major responsibility for the infection of Anti-D that occurred in 1976–77:

> The conclusion must be that he bears the major responsibility for what occurred in 1976/77 which was the largest single event contributing to the infection of Anti-D with hepatitis C.
>
> Dr O'Riordan . . . above all other, should have recognised the danger of what had occurred (*Tribunal of Inquiry Report*, pp. 24–5) .

Ms Cecily Cunningham, the biochemist who ran the laboratory where Anti-D was manufactured, also bore 'an important and serious responsibility' for the infected plasma. In 1991 she ignored warning signs arising from a form of positive hepatitis C test, 'due apparently to indifference.'

Dr Terry Walsh who had particular responsibility for donors was, the report said, in neglect of his duty when he failed to discontinue using Patient X's plasma the moment he learned of her hepatitis and jaundice. He was strongly criticised also for his failure to act when, in 1991, he received a letter from the Middlesex Hospital, confirming that Patient X's plasma was contaminated. His response to this was described as 'a vague hope that by ignoring the problem it would go away'.

In response to complaints made repeatedly by members of Positive Action about the inappropriateness of being counselled by the very people who had caused the problem, the report found the BTSB to have been 'somewhat inadequate' in its reaction to the problems of testing, informing and counselling people 'by reasons of insensitivity and also of delay and lack of information'. In addition, there was criticism of the BTSB's failure to facilitate any alternative to circulating a letter from Positive Action seeking contact with other victims of hepatitis C.

The National Drugs Advisory Board was roundly criticised for failing to make an annual inspection of the premises and procedures of the BTSB, and for failing to carry out the necessary examination and inspection of the Anti-D product. The NDAB had also failed, the report said, to carry out its function in advising on the granting of a manufacturing licence for Anti-D. Similarly, the Minister and the Department of Health had failed to supervise the National Drugs Advisory Board in licensing Anti-D, and had not provided adequate resources for the appropriate inspections and investigations to ensure that the product was safe.

The Department's policy of backdating licences to hide breaches of regulations was described as:

> quite an improper and wrong attempt to cover up by an official, rather than part of a normal if undesirable procedure (*Tribunal of Inquiry Report*, p. 153).

When it came to the politicians, Brendan Howlin was given a rap on the knuckles for not setting up independent counselling earlier and for the lack of proper supervision of the BTSB on the procedure for recall of victims. Minister Noonan's actions were described in terms of adequate responses in the circumstances.

'I have been vindicated,' said a relieved Mr Noonan. But his pleasure was to be short-lived. Controversy over the state's legal strategy adopted in the late Mrs McCole's case, and the question of his involvement in it, would follow Mr Noonan into the next change of government. It would stalk him like a ghost.

In contrast to the Beef Tribunal, which had been long drawn-out and inconclusive, and had cost the taxpayer in excess of £35 million, Judge Finlay's investigations had achieved what they set out to do. What the Tribunal had not done, however, was to investigate the separate facts around the death of Mrs McCole. There also remained the key question of accountability: would justice be seen to be done, and was the Tribunal likely to result in any prosecution of those found to be responsible?

In March 1997 the findings of the Tribunal were sent by Minister Noonan to the Director of Public Prosecutions. In October 1997, having considered the report, Mr Eamon Barnes DPP, decided not to initiate criminal prosecutions, saying that it was not possible to pursue a case under criminal law 'as it stands at the moment' .

None of the key officials named in the report as negligent continues to work for the BTSB. Ms Cecily Cunningham left after a lengthy period of sick-leave. Dr O'Riordan enjoys a quiet retirement with a handsome pension. Dr Terry Walsh retired from the BTSB early, with a golden handshake from the state, of £440,000. He is still involved in the business of blood, running his own private medical centre, which offers a screening service for paternity testing — a service that was previously provided by the BTSB. Dr Walsh also runs a high-tech DNA blood-testing service. For a while, two members of staff employed by the BTSB were also working with Dr Walsh in his private clinic, 'in their spare time'.

Chapter Twleve
A Clean Bill of Health

The Tribunal of Inquiry had revealed a shocking catalogue of errors by the Blood Transfusion Service Board.
The politicians, by contrast, had emerged relatively un-
scathed. But surely they had to shoulder some of the
blame for what had happened. How had our public representatives and the civil servants in their departments
responded to the needs of those 1,600 citizens, whose
lives had been ruined by state negligence?

What action, for instance, had then Health Minister
Brendan Howlin taken when what he described as the
'momentous crisis' landed on his desk in February 1994?
From his government office in Hawkins House, Dublin 2,
how did he react to the urgent cries for help that were
coming from Positive Action?

His successor was Michael Noonan — just how
committed was he to the 'openness and transparency'
that the rainbow coalition had promised? Did he summon
all of his political cunning to make sure that there was a
just, fair and humane solution for Mrs McCole and the
other victims? And what of the question left unanswered:
what part had the state in general and Minister Noonan
in particular played in the aggressive legal strategy used
against a dying woman?

One of the most startling facts to emerge from the Tribunal of Inquiry was that throughout his period of office

in charge of the hepatitis C crisis, Minister Howlin chose to leave the problem in the hands of those who had caused it — the Blood Bank. Never once, the Tribunal heard, had he met any of the officials in charge to demand to know what was going on or to check that the safeguards he had ordered were actually being implemented.

Leaving responsibility for sorting out the mess to the BTSB was all the more amazing when one takes into account that the Minister was well aware of their reluctance to co-operate. His officials reported difficulty in getting information. Staff in the Blood Bank were blocking the flow of information to Miriam Hederman O'Brien's Expert Group — the working group that he himself had appointed to investigate the tragedy. As senior official in the Department of Health, Donal Devitt, later reported, the Expert Group was having 'serious difficulties' in extracting relevant information from senior medical and technical staff at the Blood Bank :

> There was a reluctance to give information and there was uncertainty about the reliability of information given.

Pointing to the series of errors for which the BTSB was responsible and the distrust that Positive Action clearly had in the organisation, James Nugent SC, Counsel at the Tribunal of Inquiry, put the question bluntly to Mr Howlin:

> Did it not occur to you that whatever solutions you had to supply to the problem, the BTSB should be removed as far as they could from the scene?

Mr Howlin responded that Mr Nugent was looking at things with the benefit of hindsight.

Again, commenting on the difficulty of getting accurate information from the BTSB, James Nugent asked: 'Did you ever think of calling in the chairman and saying, "No more prevaricating"?'

Apparently the Minister did not — not even when he discovered that the current stock of Anti-D, imported from abroad, to replace existing stocks was not licensed, contrary to what he had been told by the BTSB.

It seemed that Minister Howlin's only intervention in the BTSB was the appointment, six months after the scandal broke, of a new chairman of the board, a position that had become routinely vacant.

Another equally disturbing question was why Minister Howlin had failed to make public the second source of infection that had come from Patient Y in 1989 (as dealt with in Chapter Seven). In all of his public statements, 1977 was the only year he referred to. Yet from the very start Minister Howlin's Department was told of the suspicion that infected Anti-D made from Patient Y was still in use.

This meant that contaminated batches were still in hospitals and that women who had contracted hepatitis C after 1977 were not being detected or treated. It was a delay that caused huge anger among women when the full facts were eventually disclosed.

The failure of Minister Howlin's Department to publicise the second infection was baffling. Within the BTSB itself, Dr Joan Power and Dr Emer Lawlor expressed concern. A letter pointing to suspect doses manufactured from 1991 onwards was drafted by them. They wanted the Department of Health to circulate the letter to general practitioners. The Department refused. Lack of national publicity about the second batch, coupled with the fact that all current infected batches had not been completely withdrawn by the BTSB, resulted in eight women receiving infected Anti-D in the five months after Mr Howlin learned of the scandal.

And yet again there was the question of why Mr Howlin opted for an Expert Group report — which would have no powers to compel witnesses or documents. By contrast, a tribunal of inquiry would have wide-ranging powers. At the centre of the investigation was a state organisation which was effectively blocking the flow of information. Among others, senior official Donal Devitt urged the Minister to have a sworn inquiry. If the Expert Group was not being given evidence, wasn't there cause to establish such a tribunal? The Minister thought not and the Tribunal found in his favour on this.

There were immediate practical issues too. In their document 'Altered Livers — Altered Lives', which was submitted to the Minister, Positive Action outlined in detail the immediate financial help that members needed:

> In some instances loss of income has been considerable. Financial worries have, for many families, added to the anxiety of hepatitis C. . . . No financial deterrent should be put in the way of women availing of testing and treatment.

While there was a scheme to cover out-of-pocket medical and travelling expenses, it was not working. Ironically and humiliatingly, it was administered by those at fault, the BTSB.

As revealed to the Tribunal of Inquiry, Mr Howlin's response to Positive Action's urgent pleas for financial help is telling. He said that it was: 'a suggestion made from the top of my head at the time, that they go to the community welfare officer.' James Nugent, SC, continued to question the Minister:

> Q. After this top-of-the-head advice, did you notify the community welfare officers?
>
> A. No I did not. Members of Positive Action were well able to speak up for themselves if they wanted something done.

Once again the official response fell woefully short of what required. Much of Brendan Howlin's evidence to the Tribunal of Inquiry centred round an assumption that the crisis was being properly handled by the BTSB and also by the civil servants in his own department.

So was his trust well placed? What role did the Department of Health play in safeguarding the public good?

Findings from the *Expert Group Report* and the later Tribunal of Inquiry showed that the Department of Health had failed utterly to protect the public interest. The appalling truth was that for fourteen years, between 1970 and 1984, the BTSB had been breaking the law by manufacturing Anti-D without the licence it was required to have under the Therapeutic Substances Act — without any licence at all.

More disgraceful still was that the Department of Health and the National Drugs Advisory Board (NDAB) had actively colluded in concealing licensing requirements, in that for ten years after 1984, licences were backdated and rubber-stamped. Notices of renewal were sent out years after the licences had expired. As if this wasn't bad enough, such a backdated licence had been issued just days after the BTSB had admitted the crisis.

The Tribunal of Inquiry found that

> . . . in the years from 1975 to 1994 successive Ministers of Health and the Department of Health failed adequately and appropriately to supervise the NDAB in the exercise of its functions concerning the licensing of the manufacture of products by the BTSB and the authorisation of products by the BTSB. . . (*Tribunal of Inquiry Report*, p. 104)

Lack of appropriate resources to do their job was said to be one of the key reasons. If such resources had been provided, the report said, and appropriate inspections and investigations made, it was likely that the reactions of recipients to Anti-D would have been revealed and that persons involved in the BTSB would have made further investigations than they did if they were aware of the likelihood of further inspections and interrogation. The report concluded:

> To that extent but to that extent only it would appear that
> failure of the Department to supervise the NDAB with re-
> gard to these matters and the consequential failure of the
> NDAB properly to carry out its duties of inspection and
> assessment in this context has contributed to the infection
> of Anti-D with hepatitis C (*Tribunal of Inquiry Report*, p. 105)

In other words, if the job of department officials had been
done properly, lives might have been saved.

Then there was the question of screening for hepatitis
C. As early as 1987 the Blood Bank had begun writing to
the Department of Health seeking authorisation for the
screening of donors for hepatitis C. At the time, screening
results were not 100 per cent accurate, but by 1989 a more
accurate test had become available and was being used in
many other countries. Again the Blood Bank wrote to the
Department of Health asking for its implementation. The
response was negative.

By 1990 there was increasing pressure to introduce the
test, not just from the Blood Bank, who by this time had
expressed 'extreme concern', but also from a number of
blood specialists. Finally, in 1991, after the Department
had been told by the BTSB that the test was 'imperative',
it was forced into agreeing that the long-overdue test
should be introduced.

However, that wasn't the end of the matter. Astonishing-
ly, departmental officials waited another four months before
telling the BTSB that the test had been authorised. It was a
bureaucratic delay which, the Tribunal of Inquiry heard,
had resulted in at least six people contracting the virus
from blood transfusions they had received at that time. An
emotional Gerard Hogan of the organisation Transfusion
Positive told the Tribunal that twenty of his members had
contracted hepatitis C from contaminated blood transfusions between 1989, when the BTSB had started asking for
testing, and 1991, when the tests were actually implemented.

In December 1994, the Fianna Fáil/Labour government fell. In its place was a new coalition government, with Michael Noonan in the hot seat as Minister for Health. The man known as 'the safest pair of hands in Fine Gael' had inherited the hepatitis C legacy.

Here was a chance for the Minister to acknowledge the terrible hurt felt by victims and to provide the answers to the questions they were so desperately seeking, by ensuring that the full truth was told. All along, Positive Action had insisted that the issue was not about money, but about justice.

One of Michael Noonan's first tasks was in regard to the *Expert Group Report* commissioned by his predecessor Brendan Howlin. It was presented for his prior inspection in January 1995. It was to be the official, definitive investigation into a terrible wrong that had been committed by the state. Although the report provided a damning indictment of the BTSB, it was not able to give the full picture. Scanning the report before publication, one of Mr Noonan's officials discovered that the section regarding licences contained important inaccuracies. In a memo to the Assistant Secretary of the Department, Mr Donal Devitt, she advised him of two important elements: firstly, the report revealed that for fourteen years the BTSB had manufactured Anti-D without a licence; and secondly, the report itself contained the false impression that no such licence was required.

This information was in turn forwarded to the Minister. Mr Devitt told the Tribunal that although he did not consider the matter to be of 'any major significance', he did inform Mr Noonan that the Expert Group 'didn't make any reference to the fact that the BTSB had been operating without a licence for fourteen years'. Therefore, whilst Mr Noonan knew that what was to be the definitive report into a major public health scandal did not deal with a key aspect of public oversight of the BTSB, he nevertheless went ahead and published. While providing important new evidence of the Blood Bank's role, the report contained a false picture of the part played by the Department of Health in the safeguarding of public health. Interestingly, the information, or misinformation, on licensing had been supplied by the Department itself.

One of the many disturbing facts the Expert Group uncovered was that licences had been backdated by officials of the Department. But Minister Noonan saw no reason to investigate this serious breach of duty. He told the Tribunal of Inquiry:

> As far as I was concerned, the Expert Group had reported fully, and it wasn't for me to re-investigate as Minister. . . . At no time did I feel that I should do anything further and I was not so advised.

Michael Noonan was anxious to get the whole matter sorted out — very anxious. In early 1995 he began pushing for a compensation tribunal. It would be 'speedy', 'fair' and would certainly save tax-payers money. But Positive Action did not agree. There were big problems with the type of tribunal Minister Noonan was proposing. Such a tribunal would be 'no fault', with no legal admission of liability or apology by the state. Claimants would also have to waive all rights to take legal actions. And there were further considerations regarding long-term healthcare which, the group argued, had to be sorted out. Taking a proactive stance, Positive Action insisted on an admission of liability from the BTSB and a statutory compensation scheme.

But Minister Noonan had decided how the game was to be played. And he made the rules clear. Victims could either go to his compensation tribunal, where negligence would not be an issue, or go to the High Court where they would have to prove liability.

There would be 'uncertainties, delays, stresses, confrontation and costs involved in High Court litigation', said an uncompromisingly tough letter sent by the state solicitor to women who had already issued High Court plenary summonses. And the state would 'fight all cases taken to court, going if necessary to the Supreme Court'.

Take the money, don't look for any admission of liability from the BTSB — and stop asking awkward questions, was the underlying message.

Despite protestations coming from Positive Action and the daily attacks from Dáil opposition deputies, Michael Noonan would not budge. He even refused to extend the deadline for the compensation tribunal until Brigid McCole's crucial High Court case had been heard.

It was a strategy of damage limitation, of holding the departmental line. It may well have worked, but two things got in the way: the discovery of the famous 'missing file', and Mrs McCole's death.

The 'missing file' had been discovered during the search for documents in the Brigid McCole case. It showed that the BTSB had known from 1976 to 1977 that Patient X had infectious hepatitis and not 'jaundice of unknown origin', as had been stated to the Expert Group.

Opinions differed as to the significance of the file. Minister Noonan said that the information in the file constituted no real new evidence in view of what was known about hepatitis C at the time. The findings of the Tribunal regarding this file are dealt with in Chapter Six above.

Positive Action and prominent opposition deputies argued that it put things in a totally different light. Instead of being a dreadful accident, an Act of God, here was shocking new evidence which showed that there had been terrible negligence by the BTSB. The group called for the discontinuation of the compensation tribunal and a judicial inquiry to be put in place.

Positive Action also requested that the Director of Public Prosecutions be called in to investigate whether a criminal offence had been committed.

However, it was the death of Brigid McCole on 2 October that changed everything, sending shockwaves around the nation and finally bringing home the full horror of the hepatitis C saga.

A Tribunal of Inquiry was now inevitable. Ironically, however, although it was Mrs McCole's death that made the Tribunal unavoidable, one crucial question was judged to be outside its frame of reference. This was the McCole family's 'Question 5', which referred to the state's role in the harsh and insensitive legal tactics used against their mother. The decision of the Tribunal of Inquiry not to include this in its terms of reference left a grieving family angry, frustrated and still looking for answers.

Chapter Thirteen
Behind Closed Doors

Brigid McCole versus the State was a case that wouldn't go away, even after her tragic death. The full story had not yet been heard.

'All my mother ever wanted was the simple truth,' her daughter Bríd McCole said between sobs at the Tribunal of Inquiry. But in seeking the truth Mrs McCole encountered every legalistic obstacle the state could muster. She was denied anonymity (an issue that was hugely important to all the hepatitis C victims); not allowed an early trial, despite the seriousness of her medical condition; and finally threatened with huge costs. Minister Michael Noonan stood back and watched while all this was happening. His hands were tied, he said.

The McCole family demanded to know why their dying mother had been subjected to such cruel treatment. They wanted to know exactly what role the state had played in the legal process and in particular what Minister Noonan's part in it had been. This burning political issue was one that was taken up with particular enthusiasm by the Fianna Fáil opposition spokesperson on health, Deputy Brian Cowan. Accusing both Ministers Howlin and Noonan of seriously mishandling the blood scandal, he declared that Brendan Howlin had shown 'the moral fibre of a second-hand car salesman', and that Mr Noonan had 'aided and abetted them [the BTSB] in their cover-up in the McCole case'. In a pre-election promise the leaders of Fianna Fáil and the Progressive Democrats gave a 'solemn pledge' that if elected to government they would open the files on the Brigid McCole case and would make public all relevant state documents regarding the previous government's legal strategy.

Throughout the controversy Michael Noonan steadfastly maintained that BTSB and state legal strategies were conducted separately. He subsequently claimed that he had been 'informed' of what was going on, but 'was not asked to make a policy decision'. He continued:

> Whether deputies like it or not the BTSB is a separate legal entity. It would be totally improper of me to try and give a direction on the matter.

However, his cabinet colleague, Brendan Howlin, appeared to reveal a much more active role. On RTÉ's *Liveline* programme in March 1997, Marian Finucane asked him:

> Why was the BTSB allowed to make legal threats to the McCole family when it was known that they [the BTSB] had no defence?

She was echoing the thoughts of many listeners. Brendan Howlin's reply was that the legal strategy was decided by the government and the Minister:

> The government is collectively responsible for government strategy in all these matters and advice comes through the Minister at the time, and the government made the decision in relation to how these things happened.

When questioned later about Mr Howlin's comments, Mr Noonan said that Brendan Howlin had been 'popped a question and his answer was based on faulty memory'. Mr Howlin was 'mistaken . . . he disremembered' (*Irish Times*, 6 August 1997).

At the time, increasingly stormy Dáil sessions reflected

the intense anger that was felt about Mrs McCole's treatment. Opposition deputy Liz O'Donnell of the Progressive Democrats blamed Minister Noonan for the way in which Mrs McCole was being harassed in her court case and for the lack of information that was being given to the Oireachtas. She said that there was no distinction between state liability and BTSB liability.

> Knowledge is power and in this affair all the knowledge, all the power has been in the hands of the executive and its agencies. The Dáil has been left to make what it could from the crumbs which have been extracted by way of Dáil questions and debates. There has been a cover-up of facts from the very beginning.

In August 1997, the long and bloody battle for the truth was finally brought to a conclusion. Brian Cowan, Minister for Health and Children in the new Fianna Fáil/PD government, fulfilled his party's pre-election promise by publishing the McCole report which revealed the legal strategy involved in the McCole case. The report, compiled by Senior Counsel Fidelma Macken, made public state documents that the previous government had said could not be published.

The major revelation in the report was that as early as April 1995 Michael Noonan and the rainbow coalition had been advised by the Attorney General, Dermot Gleeson, that the BTSB was negligent in making Anti-D in 1976 and from 1991 to February 1994. To put it bluntly, the BTSB hadn't a legal leg to stand on.

There were other damning revelations. Even though Mr Gleeson believed that there was no evidence available to suggest any other probable source of the infection, he still advised the government that it would be up to the claimant to obtain evidence that the contaminated Anti-D was to blame. This roundly placed the burden of proof on the women. The logic of Mr Gleeson's advice was that the victim would be forced to prove her own case. Clearly this would put the women involved at an immediate psychological disadvantage.

The Attorney General also made clear that in any legal proceedings against the state, the BTSB and the NDAB, it was 'imperative' that under no circumstances should any indication of negligence or legal liability on their part be admitted.

Such advice surely raises huge questions regarding the role of the Attorney General. Is it right, for instance, that so much power be vested in one office? Any government would presumably take his advice, so should we instead have two or more Attorneys General? Looked at from a different angle, what the Attorney General was doing was protecting tax-payers' money. We must ask ourselves certain fundamental questions: what kind of state do we, as citizens, want to live in? Is it one that protects our individual interest or one that protects our collective interests? Has the Celtic Tiger mentality become so all-pervasive that money comes before people?

Early on, in 1995, although Mr Noonan and his cabinet colleagues had been advised that the BTSB was liable, they were advised to keep their mouths tightly shut, and they did so. They remained silent while they pushed women to sign away their legal rights and to accept a narrow compensation tribunal. They looked the other way when frightening letters were being sent to hundreds of other women who, in desperation, were opting for the High Court route. The Minister knew that the BTSB was in an indefensible position when the *Expert Group Report* was being published and when Positive Action was crying out for a statutory tribunal. Yet he said nothing — although he knew it as he sat across the table at the numerous meetings he and his department officials had with Positive Action. Forty-two-year-old Paula Kiely was present at the meetings. She has early cirrhosis of the liver.

> I sat across that table with Michael Noonan and tried very
> hard to negotiate for healthcare and a statutory tribunal and
> now I realise that all that time he knew that the BTSB had no
> defence in any case against any of the women. I find that
> very hard to understand.

The National Women's Council slated the handling of the
McCole case, accusing the government of a 'breathtaking
absence of humanity'.

Jane O'Brien of Positive Action described the intense
lobbying in which her group had been involved:

> There wasn't a member of the rainbow parties who did not
> know how important it was to have an admission of liability
> and the permanence of a statutory compensation scheme.
> There was tea and sympathy from members of the cabinet,
> but nothing appeared to break down the determination that
> compensation issues should be dealt with behind closed
> doors where negligence would not be an issue.

Summing it up, Brian Cowan described the strategy as a
'carrot and stick' approach.

> The carrot was the existence of the compensation tribunal
> where negligence was preserved and where a claimant
> would not be subjected to cross-examination. An early
> hearing was also an advantage. In contrast was the strategy
> employed in the McCole case [the stick].

The aggressively adversarial approach used by the lawyers against Mrs McCole suited the government, as a
letter from the Attorney General to the Chief State Solicitor, sent on 28 September 1995, showed. Opposing Mrs
McCole's wish to use an alias had a 'tactical value' in
promoting the government's compensation scheme, the
Attorney General said.

As Brigid McCole's health visibly deteriorated, Minister Noonan and his colleagues sat by watching, as what

Deputy Máire Geoghegan-Quinn described as 'jackboot tactics' were being used. But for a full two months before Mrs McCole had ever begun her court case they had been advised that the BTSB was liable. Not until seventeen months after the coalition government had received advice from the Attorney General was liability finally admitted by the BTSB.

Another extraordinary issue raised in the McCole report was that the state failed to tell the BTSB, in April 1995, what the Attorney General's legal opinion had been: that the BTSB was negligent and was liable to pay compensation to its victims. Had it done so, Mrs McCole's case could well have been settled earlier. The BTSB could have admitted liability from the outset and she would have been spared the intense anguish that she was made to suffer.

But Minister Noonan stood firmly by the letter of the law. The value of the compensation route, he argued, was that it would save the tax-payer money, and would mean less pain for the victims. What he didn't understand was that part of the pain felt by women was caused by the fact that they were being denied the truth. There may well have been other, less altruistic considerations involved in his decision. Were there to be an admittance of negligence, there would have had to have been an earlier inquiry. And such an inquiry would no doubt bring to light not only the failing of the BTSB, but also the failing of his own Department and the NDAB. Keeping mum protected his government from the political fall-out.

The McCole family weren't for a minute convinced by Mr Noonan's account of his hands-off approach to the BTSB. Studying the report of their mother's case they said that they suspected that there must have been 'some communication' between the state and the BTSB about the BTSB's liability. It was hard to believe that 'nobody either verbally or in writing advised the BTSB that they had no defence.'

There was also the matter of the infamous letter, sent to Mrs McCole by the BTSB on 20 September. Although admitting liability, it did not concede aggravated or exemplary damages. And there was the sting in the tail — the letter also threatened that she would be liable for costs if she pursued these damages and lost. It was this threat that finally broke the resolve of a dying woman, forcing her to settle for a mere £175,000 in a desperate effort to protect her family.

Brian Cowan claimed in the McCole report that Mr Noonan had been shown, and had not changed the letter:

> The Minister for Health was shown this letter in advance of it being sent to Mrs McCole. There was no alteration made following the Minister's review of the letter.

'Bunkum,' was Michael Noonan's response:

> I didn't see the letter before it was issued. I'd like to know on what evidence he [Mr Cowan] makes that statement. Fidelma Macken makes no such allegation.

However, Fidelma Macken clearly states:

> (The) Department of Health was informed shortly prior to September 20 1996 that the letter was to be sent and was given sight of it for observation.

Added to this is the fact that an interdepartmental memo sent at this time advised that the letter be issued, 'unless the Minister disagrees'.

Mr Noonan denied seeing the letter. Since this was such a major change of policy and the first ever admission of liability by the BTSB, the Minister should surely have been made aware of its content. And if he did see it, why didn't he change the threatening clause?

In response to criticisms of the threatening clause, Mr Noonan said, 'I do not think they were threatening her.'

The letter had been interpreted as a threat, he conceded, but 'it was not sent to Mrs McCole at all', but to her lawyers.

> I would have thought that, at that point in the proceedings, it would have been possible for her legal team to explain to her that this is effectively what they (the BTSB) were saying — there is an apology, there is an admission of liability and costs will be indemnified.

The letter was merely normal legal practice, according to Mr Noonan — just like the rest of the handling of the McCole situation. But Mrs McCole, her family, her legal team and the other victims who were watching her High Court case so anxiously saw it in a very different light.

Sticking to the legal niceties appears to sum up the Minister's whole attitude with regard to the handling of the McCole case. He has argued that the report drawn up by Fidelma Macken upholds his part in it, and that because of the legal rules of the game he was prevented from intervening in any way. He quotes from her:

> Ms Macken says, inter alia, 'that the BTSB was not under the control of the Minister or answerable to him', and that she could find nothing in the regulations 'which gives the Minister any control over its activities or how it operates.'

It was the legal rules of the game, Mr Noonan stoutly insisted, which precluded him from acting in any other way. He had been exonerated by the Finlay and the Macken reports, he insisted. And if he had the time over again, he added, he could not have acted otherwise.

Sadly, the one action for which Michael Noonan may be remembered in his handling of the hepatitis C crisis is when he stood up in the Dáil and admonished Mrs McCole for having the audacity to challenge the state in court, rather than meekly accepting his no-fault compensation tribunal. Mrs McCole had died less than a week earlier.

Brian Cowan gained great political mileage from his predecessor's approach. He had challenged Michael Noonan at every possible opportunity. In his stinging report based on Fidelma Macken's findings he argues that a very different course of action could have been taken by Mr Noonan.

Speaking of an approach that was 'bereft of compassion or sensitivity', Brian Cowan says that since the state was the ultimate paymaster, it was 'in a position to call the shots and arrange an early solution to the problem'. There had been many opportunities to communicate the position to the BTSB without compromising its court defence.

> He treated this case as if it were an ordinary personal injury action instead of acknowledging and reacting to the true position, which was that Mrs McCole was a victim of the greatest health scandal in the history of the state.

But would Brian Cowan really have acted any differently had he been Minister at the time? After all, the scandal stretches over several administrations, in which all of the country's main parties have held power. The issue has become a political football — something which further victimises those affected. The reality is that all politicians want power, and our elected representatives will almost invariably put that desire for power before idealism. So government tries to hide the wrong in order to maintain power, and when it all starts to seep out, the opposition parties use the innocent victims as a stick with which to beat the government — not because they care any more or less for the victims than their opponents, but because they see it as a means of gaining power. There is every reason to believe that had the roles been reversed, government and opposition would have automatically acted in exactly the same way — the government to maintain power, and the opposition to get hold of power.

Brian Cowan's political expediency has been more than

evident — the fact that the Macken report was released on a Friday evening, whilst Michael Noonan was out of the country, is an extraordinary coincidence. Mr Cowan was also forced to:

> 'accept' Mr Noonan's assertion that he did not see, in advance, the letter from the BTSB to Mrs McCole's solicitor warning that if she sought aggravated damages and lost, costs would be sought (*Irish Times*, 7 August 1997).

The final exchanges between the two politicians descended into a political dog-fight, doubly appalling for the victims, and suggesting that really they were no more than political fodder.

There is yet another, more frightening, question that emerges, however. And that is, where does real political power lie? Are ministers as powerful as we think they are, or are they, essentially, simply puppets of their departments? They must seek and take advice from various quarters. If the advice is wrong, they carry the can — and we are free to vote them out of power. But is it not the faceless people behind the scenes who pose the real threat to us? After all, their jobs are secure — we can never vote them out of office.

Chapter Fourteen
Blood, Sweat & Tears

It is four years since the 'worst public health scandal in the history of the state' first became news. In that time there have been an expert report, a judicial inquiry, over thirty-seven special Dáil debates and acres of newsprint on the issue. But to date, not one of those responsible has been brought before the courts. Instead they have all walked free, some rewarded with generous golden handshakes.

Such a glaring injustice would not have been tolerated in many other countries where legislation allowing for prosecution is available. In France, for example , a similar blood scandal resulted in the director of the blood service, Dr Michel Garretta, receiving a four-year prison sentence for fraudulent vending, in 1992. He has since been charged with conspiracy to poison. His senior research chief and two other lower-ranking officials were also brought to court. Not only that, but the career of the former socialist prime minister, Mr Laurent Fabius, has been seriously damaged by the scandal. The pertinent question still being asked in France is whether ministers should be held responsible for decisions taken by those under them.

Successive Irish governments, of all parties, stand open to the charge of failing to make state officials legally responsible for their actions. It has taken the persistent lobbying of Positive Action and the McCole family to ensure that the issue of criminal negligence has not been allowed to rest. Justice must be seen to be done, they have argued, echoing the sentiments of many. In November 1997, Positive Action met Fianna Fáil Health Minister Brian Cowan and the Attorney General, Mr David Byrne, and presented a petition containing 9,000 signatures, calling for a full investigation into Mrs McCole's death. It was also requested that 'every possible avenue be explored to ensure there is full accountability for the Anti-D scandal'.

At present the Garda National Bureau of Investigation is studying new evidence and letters of complaint sent by the McCole family and Positive Action. If Garda Commissioner Patrick Byrne considers that there is a case, the matter will be referred to the Director of Public Prosecutions. Criminal prosecutions, which could involve the charge of manslaughter, may or may not result. Either way, it promises to be a lengthy, drawn-out process. The DPP previously decided that the case was one that could not be brought to court under current law.

The hepatitis C scandal has provoked many disturbing questions. One of these concerns the way in which our state institutions function. Ultimately, we must ask whose interests the state itself serves. Does it place the welfare of its citizens above all else, or does it function only to protect its own narrow interests?

When one state institution, the BTSB, poisoned hundreds of women and men, defences were immediately raised. The first statement issued by the Blood Bank was a chilling foretaste of how matters would be handled. Victims were told that an unfortunate accident had occurred, but that life must go on.

The BTSB was dismissive and belittling of what had happened. Important information was withheld and questions were discouraged. The government colluded in maintaining the charade, leaving the handling of the affair to those who had caused it, the Blood Bank.

When Mrs McCole and others persisted in asking awkward questions, the attitude of the state hardened. The paternalistic approach changed, and in its place hard-ball legal tactics were adopted. Women who believed that court action was their only chance of getting to the real truth felt pressurised and bullied. They were left in no doubt that the BTSB would use every legal trick in the book to avoid having to admit negligence. And in the background, hidden behind a shield of legal defences, was a government, the minister and his Department. Ranks closed. Victims were told to 'prove it' when even the dogs in the street knew that the BTSB had committed a terrible wrong.

Such an adversarial response seems common to many of our state institutions. At all levels they often appear to be hierarchical, arrogant and patronising. They function in a remote, dehumanising way, discouraging dialogue or co-operation. The implication seems to be that because ordinary people can't understand complex issues, we should allow the 'experts' to run the show. Just as the Blood Bank dismissed women by telling them, in so many words, to 'go home and stop worrying', so too did the Minister for Health decide that he knew what was in their best interest.

It is an attitude which denies us the right to make choices for ourselves, and it occurs when those in positions of power are not held responsible for their actions.

When an institution becomes more important than the citizens it purports to serve, accountability and transparency are ignored. As Máire Geoghegan-Quinn wrote in her *Irish Times* column (15 March 1997), establishment thinking is 'dangerous and anti-democratic. It assumes state institutions are innocent until proven guilty and victims guilty until proven otherwise.'

Those who seek justice because they have been wronged by state institutions will quickly find themselves pitted against the full weight of officialdom. And officialdom has huge power. It has access to information and resources. And it can prolong the battle until most people become worn out, disheartened, and so disappear.

Such a ploy has been used in other situations. In 1993, for instance, the mother of Paul O'Donoghue, a profoundly handicapped boy, insisted that her son had a right to state education. She was made to fight an uphill battle — right up to the Supreme Court — in order to prevent the Department of Education from wriggling out of its statutory obligation. 'I spent years going round in circles,' she said. 'Everyone said my son was someone else's responsibility.' Finally, in 1997, Marie O'Donoghue won her case.

And in the ten-year struggle for equal social welfare rights, waged by Married Women for Equality, successive governments steadfastly refused to admit that an injustice had taken place. It was only when the women took their case to the European Court in 1994 that an equality directive dating back to 1978 was finally implemented. In all, £360 million was paid out to the 72,000 women who had been short-changed by the state and denied their democratic rights.

Trouble was also brewing in 1985 when women who had been fitted with a Dalkon Shield (a contraceptive device) urgently sought help from the government and the Department of Health when it became known that such devices were highly dangerous. The women needed immediate healthcare and crisis counselling. They also asked for assistance in making legal claims against the US manufacturer. The government offered sympathy, but the bottom-line was that as contraception in Ireland was banned, the issue had nothing to do with an Irish government. The women were left to sort out the problem for themselves.

Denying access to the truth produces a culture of secrecy. Such a culture survives in the cloistered corridors of our government departments. It is unhealthy, undemocratic and, as journalist Fintan O'Toole reminds us, 'unaccountable institutions are deadly' (*Irish Times*, 28 March 1997).

In theory, the BTSB was monitored by regular checks and balances. But clearly such checks were non-existent. If the Department of Health and the National Drugs Advisory Board were unable to ensure that the BTSB operated within the strict bounds of safety, why was this not made public? If staffing levels and lack of finance were the problem, why did the civil servants fail to bring this to the attention of government? And why did representatives on the board of the BTSB fail to highlight the urgency of the problem?

Then there is the question of what role our public representatives play on the boards of state institutions. How do they perceive their position? Did the Department of Health representative on the board of the Blood Bank convey everything that was happening back to the Department and the Minister, especially when she knew that there was the possibility of a huge problem with infected Anti-D? If she did, why was no action taken?

Speaking at the Tribunal of Inquiry, the Department representative, Dr Rosemary Boothman, said that she definitely believed that her role was 'not to carry information from the BTSB to the Department'. Instead, she saw her role as 'bringing the Department's expertise and viewpoint to the board of the BTSB'.

To break ranks with the board of the BTSB was seriously

discouraged. One board member, Councillor Sheila O'Sullivan, met with strong resistance when she made public the findings of a shocking report about current conditions in the Blood Bank. The 1995 report revealed that despite all that had already happened, Pelican House still lacked even basic hygiene, and operated a chaotic filing system. Ms O'Sullivan felt that she was expected to say nothing publicly about the BTSB.

> There was an air of secrecy surrounding BTSB business and board members like myself were expected to sit there, say nothing and rubber-stamp what was put before us. I assumed people on boards are there to look after the public interest. I'm sorry to say that's not the case.

Throughout the entire handling of the crisis the response of the state was at odds with the interests of victims.

The Minister, in particular, seemed intent on playing macho-style politics. As though on the rugby pitch, Mr Noonan kept his eyes firmly on the touchline. He would tackle the problem, he decided, with swift precision, putting into place a cost-effective compensation tribunal which would save the state money and impress cabinet colleagues.

For a while, Mr Noonan seemed to have a clear run. Most of those infected with hepatitis C were women without political power or financial clout. They would settle for what they were given — and be grateful for it.

Would the Minister and the government have played by a different set of rules had it been the GAA, the Construction Industry Federation or the Irish Farming Association that they were dealing with?

What Mr Noonan and his advisers failed to comprehend was the depth of feeling that had been aroused among women. Something insidious and deadly had invaded their bodies. Their lives, and those of their families, had been turned upside-down, changed forever.

In pursuing his set agenda of workable solutions, the Minister failed to listen, to empathise or to comprehend. Lost in the whole equation was an understanding that the state has an obligation to be compassionate as well as cost-effective.

Counselling sessions with the BTSB present were up-setting for many women. Similarly, questions regarding drug-taking, sexual activity and tattoos were inappropriate and intrusive. Even the language that was being used diminished their suffering. Their condition was referred to, in an upbeat way, as 'hep C'. The medical jargon also served to create a barrier between the daily reality of pain and trauma and the cold, clinical world of bugs and viruses.

Together with their children, women are the biggest users of the health services. They have intimate knowledge and experience of everyday health problems. Women took Anti-D in an effort to protect their future, unborn children. It was an act of caring which ironically resulted in a death sentence for many. And they trusted that those in white coats would act responsibly. Yet they were let down, betrayed by arrogant and unaccountable members of the medical profession. While many GPs have shown genuine sensitivity, they also remain part of a top-heavy, doctor-knows-best medical ethos, which continues to deny people the right to information about their own bodies.

Restoring public confidence in the Blood Bank will take more than its recent change of management, an updated computer system or a move to shining new premises in St James's Hospital in Dublin and a new southern head-quarters in Cork. It will require radical action from our politicians to make themselves and the state institutions they represent genuinely open and accountable.

The latest CJD blood scare involving an imported

British blood product has shown that the state has learned little from the lessons of the hepatitis C affair. It has also proved that the citizens of the state have no grounds for trusting those in authority to mind their health.

Whilst Minister Brian Cowan was highly vocal in his criticism of previous governments' handling of the hepatitis C crisis, he was recently forced to admit that he had been kept in the dark for almost a fortnight about the latest CJD 'red-letter' warning. The Minister was told of the suspected contamination on 1 December 1997 — five days after Department of Health officials were informed, and eight days after the Irish Medicines Board had been alerted.

Equally shocking is that a month after the authorities here were informed by the British manufacturers that the product was being withdrawn because the original donor had died after contracting CJD, the 467 Irish patients who received the affected blood product had still not been contacted. The first that they heard about it was on RTÉ television news.

One of those Irish patients who received the infected British blood product was journalist Liz Allen. Ms Allen describes her feelings of anger and frustration at the lack of information she was given and the attitude of those in authority — the Department of Health. She was forced to spend an agonising week being shuttled between the Eastern Health Board, the Department of Health and the Dublin hospital that she was attending, trying to discover whether the product used in her case was in fact part of the infected batch.

> I blame the Department of Health for its slipshod attitude and its attempts to isolate those of us who now potentially have the killer disease by not providing any centralised information service. . . ' (*Sunday Independent*, 11 January 1998).

Calls from other women echoed her anger at not being told that she was being given a blood product in the first place, and at the paucity of information on the disease, which she was given in a letter from her hospital.

> I became thoroughly disgusted that the letter failed to pro-
> vide complete details of CJD, its origins, the status of the
> donor — the implications for me when I begin having chil-
> dren, the symptoms I should look out for, and indication of
> the timeframe for when a test might be developed to detect
> its presence in the bloodstream etc. etc. (*Sunday Independent*,
> 11 January 1998).

She was told by a medical contact that the approach taken was not a medical decision, but a political one.

> When I said I was disgusted at the lack of content in the let-
> ter I received, he told me 'their approach was not to make it
> too complex.' I know that I reflected the views of the women
> who contacted me when I angrily told the doctor not to in-
> sult my intelligence by failing to provide me with details.

Liz Allen's experience, at the hands of those in charge, is one that has been voiced by many of the women who received contaminated Anti-D. A frightening situation was made infinitely more traumatic by the patronising, placatory approach of a closed bureaucratic system.

Challenging such closed institutions is a political act. Positive Action has provided a striking role model for all groups struggling on behalf of justice. And it has proved that those who have been wronged by state agencies can fight back. Their courage has now made it more difficult for any state agency or cabinet minister to treat a section of the community with such a level of disdain.

That knowledge is power, is a valuable lesson that Positive Action learnt early on. In order to challenge the BTSB the women had to gain medical expertise. They also had to become politicians — acting strategically in their use of the media, employing a top-notch legal team and

demanding resources to fund their research and campaigning.

As citizens we have a right to demand openness and
accountability from all of our state institutions. But we
must also begin to take responsibility for ourselves. We
must become our own watchdogs, constantly asking
questions, demystifying the role of the 'professionals'. We
must affirm our right to make personal choices based on
our own very valid experiences and knowledge. Such acts
of self-help will be deeply challenging to the existing
closed system of state institutions, but they will help to
create a society that is people-centred, one in which the
rights of the individual are genuinely respected — a
better society that we can be proud to call a republic.

Epilogue
'By whose blood
we are healed'

For those with hepatitis C the pain won't go away. There will be more tragic, premature deaths. Valerie will still cry with frustration because she is too tired to give time to her children; John will continue living in his secret hell, fearful that someone will discover that he has 'a dirty disease'; Kevin will remain frightened to come home in case he finds that his mum has died; and Joan and her two boys will face yet another year without a dad.

Meanwhile, the public will rush from one scandal to another, learning of generous back-handers, and corruption in high places. But the scale of human tragedy insists that hepatitis C victims will not be forgotten. We must learn from their pain and suffering. Like the X case, the hepatitis C scandal has become branded in our minds, a salutary, sad landmark in the seventy-five-year history of our state.

The BTSB continues to use the powerful, mystic symbol of the pelican as its public face. In Christian art this strange bird is depicted as a symbol of charity and an emblem of Jesus Christ, by 'whose blood we are healed'. St Hieronymus tells the story of the female pelican restoring the life of her dead young by feeding them her own blood. The story illustrates an ultimate act of compassion and giving. But for the 1,600 people living out a death sentence passed down by a negligent blood bank, the pelican means something else — an ironic, bitter reminder of betrayal.

Key Dates in the Hepatitis C Scandal

1970
: The Blood Transfusion Service Board (BTSB) begins the manufacture of Anti-D, a product made from blood plasma. Anti-D is given to mothers who have rhesus negative blood but give birth to a baby with rhesus positive blood. It helps to prevent illness, and possible death, in future rhesus positive babies.

Nov. 1976
: A pregnant woman, 'Patient X', receives multiple blood transfusions in a Dublin hospital. Plasma is taken from her without her consent, to make Anti-D. Patient X becomes jaundiced during treatment and the hospital sends plasma to the BTSB for tests. Although they are made aware that she has infective hepatitis, stocks of the plasma are later released and used.

July 1977
: The Rotunda Hospital and GPs notify the BTSB of three patients showing hepatitis-like symptoms after receiving doses of Anti-D manufactured from Patient X's blood. Existing stocks continue to be used. Between August and December 1977 four more women who received Anti-D are reported by their GPs as having hepatitis and jaundice. Still no recall of stocks by the BTSB.

Sept. 1977
: Specimens of Anti-D made from Patient X's plasma sent by BTSB to Middlesex Hospital for testing. Results inconclusive but doubt cast on the safety of using plasma. UK doctors freeze samples until better technology for testing is available. BTSB continues to use Anti-D made from Patient X's plasma.

Nov. 1977
: Brigid McCole receives Anti-D made from infected batch — one that is ultimately responsible for her death.

Aug. 1989
: 'Patient Y' begins plasma exchange treatment in St James's Hospital. A month later she becomes infected with hepatitis C from contaminated plasma received from the BTSB. Twelve plasma donations are taken from her and frozen for later use.

Jan. 1991
: Plasma from Patient Y is unfrozen and used to make Anti-D apparently without proper tests being conducted. As a result, batches of Anti-D for 1991–94 become contaminated.

Dec. 1991
: Middlesex Hospital unfreezes plasma taken from Patient X in 1977. Tests show Anti-D infected with hepatitis C and strongly suggest that this was the cause of hepatitis C outbreaks in 1977. Chief Medical Consultant of the BTSB is informed of this by fax but fails to act on this vital information.

Feb. 1994   Research by BTSB shows a high incidence of hepatitis C
               amongst women who have received the Anti-D product.
               The link is made. Department of Health is informed and
               the scandal becomes public.
               An Expert Group under Miriam Hederman-O'Brien is set
               up to investigate.

April 1995   *Expert Group Report* criticises handling by BTSB of Anti-D
               contamination issue.

March 1996   Compensation Tribunal for sufferers begins hearings.
               More than £250,000 awarded on its first day.
               Missing file discovered at the BTSB reveals that the Blood
               Bank knew that Patient X had 'infectious hepatitis' when
               it used her plasma to manufacture Anti-D. Pressure for a
               judicial inquiry mounts but it is resisted by the Minister
               for Health. BTSB makes clear that it will fully defend all
               legal actions.

Oct. 1996   Brigid McCole dies just days before her High Court action
               is due to be heard. Just prior to her death the BTSB admits
               liability, apologises and reaches a compensation settle-
               ment. Government is forced to set up a Tribunal of Inquiry.

Nov. 1996   Tribunal of Inquiry begins, lasting for three months.

March 1997   *Report of Tribunal of Inquiry* published, revealing important
               information not available in *Expert Group Report*.

July 1997   Mrs Mary Quinlan settles a two-year battle against the
               BTSB, the State and the National Drugs Advisory Board,
               just minutes before it is due to be heard in the High Court.

Aug. 1997   McCole Report, compiled by Senior Counsel Fidelma
               Macken, is published. Report makes public state docu-
               ments regarding the legal strategy adopted against Mrs
               McCole.

Oct. 1997   Director of Public Prosecutions says that criminal prose-
               cution of BTSB executives cannot be brought under cur-
               rent law.

Oct. 1997   Compensation Tribunal is put on a statutory basis.

Dec. 1997   Garda Commissioner announces criminal investigation
               into hepatitis C scandal following letters of complaint and
               fresh evidence from Positive Action and the McCole family.

Dec. 1997   Another blood scare. Patients who received a potentially
               infected British blood product are told that they are at risk
               of developing CJD (Creutzfeldt-Jakob Disease), the human
               form of Mad Cow Disease.

Who's Who? — The Main Players

Organisations
Blood Transfusion Service Board (BTSB)
National Drugs Advisory Board (NDAB), now known as Irish Medicines
    Board

Transfusion Positive
The Irish Kidney Association
The Irish Haemophilia Society

People

Dr Terry Walsh	Senior Medical Officer BTSB 1969; Assistant Director BTSB from 1976; Chief Medical Consultant BTSB from 1988; now runs private blood-testing clinic
Dr John Patrick (Jack) O'Riordan	Former National Director BTSB
Dr Joan Power	Consultant Haematologist BTSB from 1989
Dr Emer Lawlor	Part-time post as Consultant Haematologist BTSB from 1988
Cecily Cunningham	Technical Officer Fractionation Department BTSB from 1968; Principal Biochemist from 1974

Experts

Dr Whelton	Chairman of the Hepatology Group
Dr G. Duisheiko	A leading virologist and independent expert on hepatitis C
Eddie Hogan	Clinical Psychologist appointed by BTSB to run counselling sessions
Dr John Hegarty	Consultant Hepatologist; Medical Director of liver treatment unit in St Vincent's Hospital
Professor Hans Hoppe	Professor of Medicine, University of Hamburg; formerly director of Central Institute for Blood Transfusion, Hamburg. Advised BTSB in setting up its Anti-D programme
Dr David Dane	Retired Consultant Virologist
Jane O'Brien	Spokesperson for Positive Action, the driving force behind the campaign
Brigid McCole	Took the first High Court challenge as a victim of hepatitis C; died October 1996
Bríd McCole	Daughter of the late Brigid McCole
Paula Kiely	Member of Positive Action

Gerard Hogan	Past Secretary of Transfusion Positive
Rosemary Daly	Administrator of Irish Haemophilia Society
Donor L	Gave evidence at Tribunal of Inquiry, but wished to remain anonymous
Witness 1A	The woman behind the screen at the Tribunal of Inquiry, a member of the Irish Kidney Association

Lawyers
John Rogers SC	representing the McCole family and Positive Action
James Nugent SC	representing the Tribunal of Inquiry
Judge Thomas Finlay	presiding over the Tribunal of Inquiry

Politicians
Brendan Howlin TD (Labour)	Minister for Health 1993–4
Michael Noonan TD (Fine Gael)	Minister for Health 1994–7
Dr Tim Collins	Special Advisor to Brendan Howlin TD
Brian Cowan (Fianna Fáil)	Present Minister for Health (1997–)

Civil Servants
Donal Devitt	Senior Official in Department of Health who reported difficulties in getting information to Minister Howlin
Dr Rosemary Boothman	Deputy Chief Medical Officer, Department of Health; member of the board of the BTSB
Dr Miriam Hederman O'Brien	Compiled *Expert Group Report*
Fidelma Macken SC	Compiled a report into the legal strategy involved in the McCole case.